The Observer's Pocket Series

ROCKS AND MINERALS

The Observer's Book of

ROCKS AND MINERALS

FRANCES AND RICHARD ATKINSON

INCLUDING DESCRIPTIONS OF 72 MINERAL
VARIETIES AND 52 ROCK TYPES FOUND
THROUGHOUT THE WORLD. 58 COLOUR AND
7 BLACK-AND-WHITE PHOTOGRAPHS.
NUMEROUS LINE ILLUSTRATIONS

CLAREMONT BOOKS

PENGUIN BOOKS

Published by the Penguin Group
Penguin Books Ltd, 27 Wrights Lane, London W8 5TZ, England
Penguin Books USA Inc., 375 Hudson Street, New York, New York 10014, USA
Penguin Books Australia Ltd, Ringwood, Victoria, Australia
Penguin Books Canada Ltd, 10 Alcorn Avenue, Toronto, Ontario, Canada
M4V 3B2
Penguin Books (NZ) Ltd, 182–190 Wairau Road, Auckland 10, New Zealand

Penguin Books Ltd, Registered Offices: Harmondsworth, Middlesex, England

This edition first published in Great Britain in 1979 by
Frederick Warne

This revised edition published in 1996 by Claremont Books,
an imprint of Godfrey Cave Associates Limited,
42 Bloomsbury Street, London WC1B 3QJ

ISBN 1 85471 044 3

Printed in Italy

CONTENTS

ACKNOWLEDGEMENTS

The author and publishers wish to thank the following for their kind permission to reproduce photographs:

British Museum (Natural History), pages 45, 48 (below), 52, 53, 57 (below), 60, 61 (both), 64 (both), 68, 69, 72, 73, 76, 77, 80 (both), 85, 88 (both), 92, 93, 96, 97, 100 (both), 101, 108, 109, 112 (both), 117 (both), 120, 124, 136, 140 (above), 145, 149, 160, 165, 173 (below).

Institute of Geological Sciences, pages 48 (above), 57 (above), 81, 84, 89, 104, 105, 121, 125, 137, 140 (below), 152, 157, 169, 173 (above).

Code for Geological Fieldwork

Readers who wish to go collecting rock or mineral specimens in the field are advised to take out insurance cover. It is also advisable, if in Britain, to obtain a copy of *A Code for Geological Fieldwork* which covers such matters as personal safety and visits to quarries, nature conservation and the conduct of field parties. The code is issued by the Geologists' Association, London.

PREFACE

The geological scope of this book is intended to be world-wide.

Its aim is to help people with no previous knowledge of geology to understand and identify rocks and minerals. The simple identification tests which are described can be carried out using nothing more complicated than a penknife, steel file, magnifying lens and dilute acid. Laboratory tests for minerals, and microscopic identification of rocks, which are of little practical use at this level, have not been described. It is possible to identify minerals without knowing the symmetry classes to which they belong, so these have also been omitted.

Where possible the chemical composition and formula of a mineral has been given. However, most silicates have such complex and variable compositions that they can only be described in very general terms.

The minerals have been arranged in the book in order of the atomic numbers of their principal elements. The arrangement was chosen to keep all the ores of a metal such as copper together instead of having the sulphides in one place, the carbonates somewhere else and the oxides in yet another section. The silicates have been grouped with quartz as silicon minerals, although silicon is not the principal element in all of them.

There are approximately 3,000 rock or mineral specimens (and their many thousand varieties) known in the world. This is far more than we could describe in a book this size, and inevitably many have been omitted. However, there are entries for most of those which are common, economically important or particularly interesting.

INTRODUCTION

We are surrounded by rocks and minerals and articles made from them. Common salt, an edible mineral, and pumice, a volcanic rock can be found in most homes. Bricks, china and pottery are made of baked clay; glass is made from quartz sand; cement is a mixture of clay and lime obtained from limestone and all the metals we use are extracted from ore minerals.

The outer layer or crust of the earth is made of different types of rocks: igneous rocks which have crystallized from a molten state; sedimentary rocks formed by the accumulation of material produced by the breakdown of other rocks; and metamorphic rocks which are igneous or sedimentary rocks altered by heat or pressure.

Rocks are aggregates of minerals, and to a geologist a mineral is a naturally occurring inorganic substance with a definite chemical composition and properties which distinguish it from other minerals. Oil or petroleum is derived from living things and therefore not a mineral in the strict sense. Nearly all minerals are crystalline and some crystals grow to enormous sizes. In the Ural mountains a quarry nine metres square has been sunk in a single felspar crystal.

Most minerals are compounds of two or more elements, but some minerals also occur as individual elements, for example copper and sulphur, and are known as native minerals. Altogether about two and a half thousand minerals are known but in ordinary rocks most are present only in minute traces. We only notice them if they have been concentrated by geological processes into mineral veins and other deposits large enough to make their extraction profitable. These valuable minerals are known as ores and are better known than the common rock-forming minerals which make up most of the earth's crust.

Man's history is marked by his use of different rocks and minerals. In the Palaeolithic period he began using as tools pebbles of flint, quartzite and other rocks that broke with a sharp edge. Later clay was used to make pottery, and a succession of metals were used for tools and ornament. The oldest objects of worked metal were excavated from Catal Huyuk in Turkey and date from 6000 to 5500 BC. They are tubes hammered out of native copper and were used to decorate a string skirt or kilt.

Smelting metals from their ores came later and was a slow and difficult process. It was not until the industrial revolution, when new methods of smelting were discovered that metals began to be used on a large scale. Since then our consumption of minerals has increased so rapidly that in the second half of the twentieth century more minerals have been extracted and used than in all the thousands of years before. At this rate, unless new resources can be found, supplies of some minerals will soon be exhausted.

FINDING ROCKS AND MINERALS

Unless you live in an area where there are rock outcrops you will have to begin by looking at pebbles, or else at rocks which have been shaped and used by man as building or ornamental stones. Kerb or paving stones, bridges and buildings such as churches, town halls and libraries are often made of stone. Houses, especially old ones, may be built of local stone. They may have slate roofs, stone pillars and steps, and inside perhaps stone floors and fireplaces. Marble is often used indoors where it is not exposed to the weather. Sandstone and limestone are the most frequently used building stones, and durable granite is one of the most popular for memorials, fountains, gravestones and drinking troughs. Some shops and banks are faced with decorative slabs of serpentine, granite, syenite, marble or slate.

Museums often have carved stone objects on show: prehistoric tools, marble statues and perhaps mineral specimens. Jewellers may also have minerals on display.

Most ores are mined, and good specimens are likely to be found on mine tips. There may be traces of ore in the rock waste, and also gangue minerals, which to a collector can be equally interesting. An old mine tip has the added advantage that minerals in hidden veins and cavities may be exposed by weathering.

Rocks are not as elusive as ore veins and are usuallly quarried from a hole in the ground. Some ores are won in this way too, usually sedimentary deposits occurring in a thick layer of considerable extent. Once the soil and rock above have been dug away the ore is simply shovelled out by mechanical digger.

Another way of extracting ore is by separating heavy minerals from placer deposits. Placers are sediments containing ore minerals weathered out of the original rock. Heavy minerals tend to accumulate in streams and rivers because they are the first to be dropped when the current slackens

Camborne mining district in Cornwall, UK

Middle Peak Quarry in massive limestone, Derbyshire, UK

while lighter minerals travel on. Gold is the best known placer mineral. By panning stream sediments, gold and other heavy minerals such a cassiterite or stream tin, magnetite, garnets, diamonds and other gems can be separated out. Mechanical separators can be used to do the work but in countries where labour is cheaper than machinery panning is still done by hand, as in the gem gravels of Burma and the tin streams of Malaysia.

If you would like to try panning yourself, find a round shallow pan, wooden dish or even a hubcap. Early prospectors used their frying pans. Find a promising stream and dig some sand from the bottom. Put a little in the pan and throw out any stones you can see, then dip the pan half into the water and move it to and fro so that the water rushes round inside. It is important to get a good swirl of water going in the pan so that the lighter minerals climb up the sides and heavy ones are left in the centre. Let a small amount of sediment wash out of the pan at each swirl until only a handful is left. Examine this with a lens for interesting minerals.

The best way to find out where to look for minerals is by visiting a museum which as a mineral collection. Note where the specimens come from and find the localities on a good map. If possible, compare this with a geological map of the area, which will show the rock types. Igneous rocks and the contacts between igneous and sedimentary rocks, especially limestones, are the best hunting grounds for minerals. Sedimentary rocks like clay, sandstone and chalk may contain nodules of various kinds.

The rocks marked on the map may be hidden below the soil so look in places where bedrock has been exposed by erosion or quarrying. Out crops are likely on high ground, in river banks, quarries, cliffs, road or railway cuttings and building sites. River beds, beaches, field and gardens are good places to look for pebbles and boulders which may have travelled miles from the outcrop where they originated.

All land belongs to someone and it is essential to obtain the owner's permission to collect material. This applies particularly to mines and quarries, even if they are no longer

Panning stream sediments

in use. You should also check whether the land is part of a Nature Reserve or National Park, or any other place where hammering is not allowed.

Collecting rocks and minerals is fascinating and rewarding, whether carried out alone or with others. Local libraries are often a good source of information regarding local geological societies where enthusiasts meet.

Obviously, railway cuttings may be visited only if the line has been closed. When examining road cuttings be careful not to dislodge stones which could be a hazard on the road. Instead of climbing, look in the scree at the foot of a cliff, cutting or quarry wall. If there are veins, cavities or a concentration of minerals along bedding planes or joints, good crystals may have weathered out and can be picked up without hammering. The rule is to hammer as little as possible. Hammering speeds up erosion and leaves unsightly scars. Hammer pieces of rock on the ground, not the rock wall itself. For safety, you should wear goggles with safety glass to protect your eyes. Holding one hand in front of your eyes is both awkward and, if the rock is very hard and chips fly, completely inadequate.

Some basic equipment is required when studying rocks and minerals: a good hand lens with a magnification of about × 10, and a geological hammer, which should have a square head and a pick or chisel edge, for field work. A penknife, a chisel for splitting open rocks and goggles, which should always be worn when hammering to protect your eyes from splinters of rock, are also useful. A hard hat is advisable in certain areas and is essential when visiting a quarry. Other basics include comfortable walking boots or shoes, sensible hardy clothes and a small rucksack to transport your finds home. Specimens should be individually numbered immediately, using a felt tip pen, either directly or on a label stuck to the specimen. The number should be entered into a notebook, together with details of the locality and date. It is also advisable to wrap specimens in newspaper, as this will avoid their being chipped.

Looking after your collection   Wash the specimen in

15

warm water with a little detergent, using a soft brush and then rinse well in clean water. This may cause your original identification label to become illegible or detached. Make sure that you can identify your specimens after they have been washed. When it is completely dry, apply a spot of white acrylic paint. This, when dry, will act as a base for a permanent identification number, which should be written neatly in Indian ink.

THE CHEMICAL COMPOSITION OF MINERALS

Each mineral has a constant, distinctive, chemical composition, which is expressed by chemical formula. Some minerals, known as the native elements, contain only one element, but an absolutely pure mineral hardly ever exists and most minerals are usually composed of a mixture of compounds and more than one element.

Compounds are comprised of two charged parts, called ions. The negatively charged anions often contain oxygen. The mixtures in various minerals are not accidental, as certain elements can exist jointly only within the boundary of the physical laws of chemistry. Galena (page 47) (PbS), for example, usually contains impurities of silver which can be replaced by lead, for the crystal structure and physical properties of galena and argentine (page 62) (Ag_2S) are closely allied.

Such a blending of chemical compounds with a similar chemical formula is termed isomorphous. It is also quite usual with minerals that under certain conditions two or more elements may replace each other. In olivine (page 107), for example, iron and magnesium are always present and often replace each other. However, the proportions of the constituent elements do vary in different olivines and this is why the formula of olivine − magnesium + iron silicate − is expressed in symbols as $(Mg, Fe)_2Si_2O_4$; the elements Mg and Fe may be substituted for each other.

Much can be learned from a chemical formula: for instance, it is possible to determine the approximate proportion of a metal, or any other useful element, present in a mineral.

Every element has a definite atomic weight (the ratio of the weight of one atom of the element to one-twelfth of the weight of one atom of carbon); it is thus sufficient to insert the corresponding numerical values into the chemical formula, then to convert them to percentages. For example, haematite (page 77) : Fe_2O_3; the atomic weight of Fe is 55.85, and the atomic weight of O is 16. The molecular weight is the sum of the total of the atomic weights of the atoms composing the molecule of the substance, thus $Fe_2O_3 = 159.70$. From this, the volume of Fe in a given quantity of Fe_2O_3 may be worked out.

COMMON ANIONIC GROUPS

Name	Formula
Aluminate	Al_2O_4
Arsenide	As
Arsenate	AsO_4
Borate	BO_3
Chloride	Cl
Carbonate	CO_3
Chromate	CrO_4
Fluoride	F
Molybdate	MoO_4
Nitride	N
Nitrate	NO_3
Oxide	O
Hydroxide	OH
Phosphate	PO_4
Sulphide	S
Silicate	SiO_4
Sulphate	SO_4
Titanate	TiO_3
Tungstate	WO_4

SYMBOLS FOR ELEMENTS

Ag	Silver
Al	Aluminium
As	Arsenic
Au	Gold
B	Boron
Ba	Barium
Be	Beryllium
Bi	Bismuth
C	Carbon
Ca	Calcium
Cl	Chlorine
Co	Cobalt
Cr	Chromium
Cu	Copper
F	Fluorine
Fe	Iron
H	Hydrogen
Hg	Mercury
K	Potassium
Li	Lithium
Mg	Magnesium
Mn	Manganese
Mo	Molybdenum
Na	Sodium
O	Oxygen
P	Phosphorus
Pb	Lead
Pt	Platinum
S	Sulphur
Sb	Antimony
Si	Silicon
Sn	Tin
Sr	Strontium
Ti	Titanium
U	Uranium
W	Tungsten
Zn	Zinc
Zr	Zirconium

GEOLOGICAL TIME CHART

Era	Period	Time (in millions of years ago)
Cenozoic	Quaternary	
		2
	Tertiary	
		65
Mesozoic	Cretaceous	
		145
	Jurassic	
		208
	Triassic	
		245
Paleozoic	Permian	
		290
	Carboniferous	
		362
	Devonian	
		408
	Silurian	
		439
	Ordovician	
		510
	Cambrian	
		570
Precambrian		

HOW ROCKS ARE FORMED

Igneous Rocks Igneous rocks crystallize from molten material called magma which rises from hot regions below the earth's surface. The main masses of magma rise very slowly, engulf the rocks in their way and push aside and distort the rocks above so that they bend and crack. The magma pushes its way between horizontal layers of rock to form sills and into vertical cracks where it may solidify as dykes. Some magma reaches the surface, to be erupted as lava.

Magma which crystallizes deep underground forms plutonic rocks, the name being taken from Pluto, the Roman god of the underworld. Magma extruded from volcanoes forms a variety of volcanic rocks. Lava sometimes flows quietly from a volcano, but it may be blown to froth or fragments by gases escaping from the magma like bubbles from champagne. These fragments become bombs, ash or pumice, deposits of which accumulate around the volcano. Magma erupted under the sea forms pillow lavas, blobs of molten rock chilled by the water. Cooled quickly on land, lava becomes obsidian or volcanic glass. A wide variety of volcanic rocks can be produced from one kind of magma.

The most abundant elements in the earth's crust are silicon and oxygen, and as magma cools these combine with other elements in it to form silicates. These are the commonest rock-forming minerals and are often divided into two groups, mafic and felsic. Olivine, pyroxenes, amphiboles and biotite, which are rich in iron and magnesium, are known as mafic or ferromagnesian minerals. They are dark coloured and heavy, compared with the felspars and quartz, which are known as felsic minerals.

Another name for silica is silicic acid and rocks containing a large proportion of silica are classed as acid rocks. The excess of silica is left over as quartz after the other silicates have crystallized. Those without quartz are known as basic

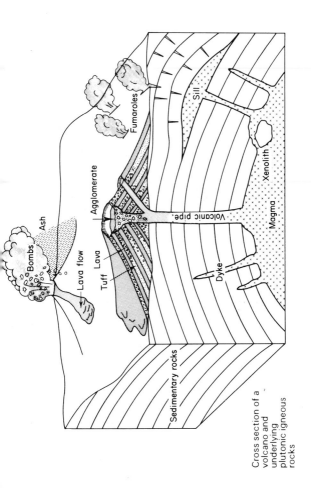

Bombs

Ash

Fumaroles

Lava flow

Tuff   Lava

Agglomerate

Volcanic pipe

Sill

Xenolith

Magma

Dyke

Sedimentary rocks

Cross section of a
volcano and
underlying
plutonic igneous
rocks

rocks, and some with very few felsic minerals are said to be ultrabasic.

The grain size of a rock is determined by the speed at which the magma cools. If magma cools slowly, large crystals have time to grow, and if they are large enough to be identified by eye the rock is termed coarse-grained. Magma that has cooled more quickly in dykes and sills forms a medium-grained rock in which crystals can be seen but cannot be identified without the help of a lens. Lava chills quickly and is fine-grained: the crystals are too small to be distinguished by the naked eye but they can be seen twinkling as the rock is turned in the light. Lava chilled so quickly that the minerals do not have time to crystallize forms volcanic glass.

The crystals may not be all the same size. A fine- or medium-grained rock with a few large crystals in it is called a porphyry. Porphyritic texture can develop where a magma containing large crystals which have formed at depth is injected into near surface rocks as a dyke or sill. The liquid portion of the magma cools rapidly, forming a fine-grained groundmass around the larger crystals.

Pegmatites are very coarse-grained igneous rocks with crystals 2 cm or more across. They are formed when the magma has nearly cooled and the residual liquids are expelled into fractures in and around an igneous intrusion.

A simple classification of igneous rocks can be based on grain size, acidity and the types of minerals the rocks contain.

Sedimentary Rocks Sedimentary rocks are made up of fragments of other rocks broken down by shattering, abrasion and chemical weathering. These fragments are carried away and deposited, usually in water, as more or less horizontal layers of sediment. These are compacted by the weight of the layers above and cemented by minerals which fill the spaces between fragments. The type of sedimentary rock produced depends on the source rock, the type and degree of weathering, and the distance the sediment travels before being deposited.

Shattering may be initiated by frost in mountain areas, by

CLASSIFICATION OF IGNEOUS ROCKS

TEXTURE	Abundance of quartz and/or light coloured felsic minerals			Abundance of dark mafic minerals, especially olivine and pyroxene		
	ACID	INTERMEDIATE		BASIC	ULTRABASIC	
	Chief felspar: potash felspar		Chief felspar: plagioclase		No felspar	
	+ quartz	− quartz	biotite and/or hornblende	pyroxene and/or olivine	− olivine	+ olivine
Coarse grained (Plutonic)	GRANITE	SYENITE	DIORITE	GABBRO	PYROXENITE	PERIDOTITE
Medium grained	MICROGRANITE	MICROSYENITE	MICRODIORITE	DOLERITE (DIABASE)	—	—
Fine grained (Volcanic)	RHYOLITE	TRACHYTE	ANDESITE	BASALT	—	—

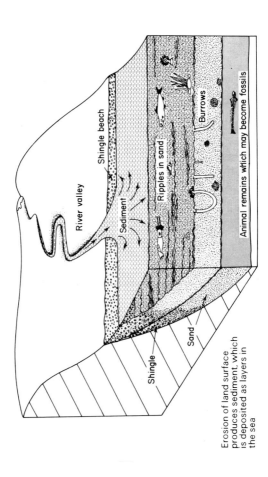

River valley

Shingle beach

Sediment

Ripples in sand

Burrows

Animal remains which may become fossils

Shingle

Sand

Erosion of land surface produces sediment, which is deposited as layers in the sea

plant roots forcing their way into cracks, or by sudden cooling of rocks that have been heated by the sun. Fragments are carried away by mass movement, running water, glaciers or the wind. The fragments are ground together in the process into smaller and smaller pieces, at the same time wearing away the rocks in their path. This means that a sediment carried a short distance and deposited quickly is usually coarse grained, like conglomerate, whereas protracted transport and abrasion reduces the pieces of rock to fine silt, or mud.

Chemical weathering is brought about by plant acids and rainwater which has become weakly acid by dissolving carbon dioxide gas from the air. The minerals in a crystalline rock may be altered to new minerals which are soft or earthy so that the rock crumbles, or they may change by the addition of water to minerals which take up more space so that the rock splits and shatters. In this way the mafic minerals alter to iron oxides, and felspars and muscovite weather into clay minerals. In the process, soluble sodium, potassium and calcium salts are released and washed away. Quartz is hardly affected at all and is left behind as a sandy residue.

Sedimentary processes are characterized by sorting, which takes place while the sediment is being transported. Sediment dumped near its place of origin tends to be unsorted and contains a variety of minerals and rock fragments of different sizes. Sediment carried by water is sorted into different grain sizes by the carrying power of the current. Fast rivers can carry large rocks as well as fine sediment but as they lose momentum, the boulders are dropped, leaving only finer material in suspension to be dropped in its turn when the current becomes more sluggish. This means that sediment which has travelled a long way is usually fairly uniform in grain size and may consist of a single mineral such as the quartz in sandstone and the clay in shale.

Chemical sediments are made up of sodium, potassium, calcium and other salts dissolved during weathering. These usually find their way to the sea and so remain in solution; but if rivers run into a lake which has no outlet and the water evaporates, the minerals are left behind. The lake then becomes salty like the Dead Sea or Great Salt Lake in Utah and continued evaporation leaves deposits of soluble salt and gypsum which are called evaporites. Evaporites also form where sea water occasionally floods into a hot dry area like the Afar Triangle, which lies near the Red Sea coast of Ethiopia. The water dries up, leaving a little calcite, thick deposits of gypsum and halite and small amounts of potassium and magnesium salts.

Other sediments deposited from solution under different conditions include oolites, iron deposits precipitated in stagnant swamps, and nodules of iron and manganese formed on the sea floor.

Certain structures are characteristic of sedimentary rocks. Sediments are normally laid down in horizontal layers which vary from thin laminae to thick beds or strata. On a dune or sandbank, however, sand is swept over the edge and comes to lie in sloping layers which may be partly eroded before another set is laid down, perhaps sloping in another direction. In this way crossbedding is produced. Structures may also be formed when sediments are exposed to the air, and then buried by a new layer of sediment. Raindrops hitting mud or fine sand can leave small circular pits, and when a sediment dries out under the sun cracks develop at the surface, a feature often seen in dried out mud. Animal tracks and burrows may be preserved, as well as fossils of plants or animals which lived in the place where the sediment was accumulating. Some rocks consist almost entirely of the remains of living things and are known as organic sedimentary rocks. Examples are limestones made up of broken shells or coral fragments, and coal and lignite which are the compressed remains of plants.

The deposition of sediment is only the beginning of rock formation. As layer after layer of sediment is laid down, the weight squeezes the sediments at the bottom of the pile and water is expelled. The platy minerals are flattened and the grains are packed tightly together so that they adhere and become a more or less solid mass. This may take millions of years and involve a burial depth of thousands of feet. After compaction the sediment often has a cementing mineral deposited by groundwater seeping through the spaces between grains. The usual cements are calcite, silica and iron minerals.

Finally, as sediments are buried and converted into rocks they may be folded and raised up to form mountains like the Rockies or Himalayas. Fossils and structures in the sedimentary rocks of which these mountains are largely composed testify that the rocks were once part of the sea floor.

Metamorphic Rocks   Metamorphic rocks are formed when rocks are subjected to conditions of temperature, pressure and chemical activity which differ from those under which they were originally formed. These new conditions bring about changes in texture and growth of new minerals. All these changes take place in the solid state, without melting the rocks.

Three broad categories of metamorphism can be recognized: (a) thermal or contact metamorphism; (b) dynamic metamorphism; (c) regional or dynamo-thermal metamorphism.

Contact metamorphism occurs when hot magma is injected into cold country rock. The heat of the intrusion literally bakes the rock around it, the effects diminishing with distance from the contact. In this way an aureole or zone of altered rocks where recrystallization has taken place is formed around any igneous intrusion, its extent depending on the size and temperature of the igneous body.

Pure sediments affected by contact metamorphism recrystallize to give a new texture but no new minerals are formed. A pure limestone becomes a marble, a pure sandstone becomes a quartzite. Rocks with a variety of minerals, such as shale, mudstone and fine volcanic rocks produce rocks known as hornfels in which new minerals such as garnet and andalusite can develop. These new minerals may grow into large crystals known as porphyroblasts.

As one walks towards the site of an igneous intrusion the

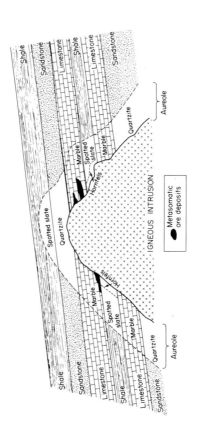

Metamorphic aureole around an igneous intrusion

first effect of the thermal metamorphism that one notices in a rock such as shale is a spotted texture caused by the growth of tiny new crystals of minerals such as andalusite. Closer to the contact, recrystallization will have produced fine-grained splintery hornfels.

Dynamic metamorphism is produced mainly by mechanical processes brought about by an increase in pressure. Growth of new minerals is relatively insignificant because of the low temperatures at which the metamorphism takes place. Changes in texture are by far the most important result.

Where pressure has built up in rocks they may fail, and a fault or thrust develops. A fault is a high angle break and a thrust is a low angle break lying nearly horizontally. Rocks on either side of these breaks are ground down by the action of rock masses moving against each other. Mylonite is produced in this way.

Pressure is also responsible for the formation of slates. Where intense folding occurs in fine-grained rocks such as shales and mudstones the pressures which produce the folding act on a very small scale to rotate all the particles

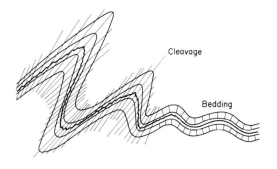

The relationship of cleavage and bedding in folded rocks

29

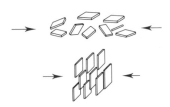

Randomly orientated platy minerals in a sediment are rotated by pressure to form the cleavage found in slates

within the sediment until they lie in planes at right angles to the directions of maximum pressure. Any growth of new platy minerals follows these parallel planes making them more apparent, and eventually all traces of the original bedding are lost. In this way the property of fissility or slaty cleavage is developed.

The boundary between dynamic metamorphism of the type that produces slates and regional, dynamo-thermal metamorphism is very arbitrary, and the two merge into one another. Temperature plays a more important role in regional metamorphism due to the greater depths of burial.

Regional metamorphism, as its name implies, occurs over extensive areas, often thousands of square miles. Deep burial within the earth's crust causes intense deformation because of the great pressures and temperatures encountered at depth. Rocks which have undergone this type of metamorphism, such as schists and gneisses, are often highly contorted and display evidence of having suffered more than one episode of metamorphic recrystallization. The Moine schists of north-west Scotland show evidence of at least four separate events.

Temperatures may become high enough within some metamorphic belts for melting to take place, and rocks known as migmatites are formed among the schists and gneisses already formed in the solid state.

The minerals found in metamorphic rocks can be used to determine how great the effect or grade of metamorphism has been. Sillimanite is found in schists and gneisses which have been subjected to very high temperatures, whilst kyanite is indicative of high pressures.

A rough guide to metamorphic grade is given by the following minerals:

LOW GRADE	MEDIUM GRADE	HIGH GRADE
Chlorite Biotite	Garnet Staurolite	Kyanite Sillimanite

Often accompanying metamorphism is a process known as metasomatism, which involves an overall change in chemical composition. New chemicals are added whilst original components are transported away by gases and hot watery solutions. The alkali metals potassium and sodium are very easily transported as simple compounds and they are often introduced into rocks thus forming potassium felspar and sodium rich plagioclase. Metasomatism is also a very important process in contact metamorphism when chemical constituents of the magma are introduced into the country rocks. Many ore bodies are formed in this way, the magnetite deposits of the Iron Springs district in Utah being an example.

THE ORIGIN OF MINERAL DEPOSITS

Mineral deposits are concentrations of minerals which can be profitably worked. They are usually called ores (though some people call only metallic minerals ores), and the economically unimportant minerals which accompany them are known as gangue.

Elements continually combine at varying temperatures and pressures to make different minerals. The common minerals make up the rocks of the earth's crust, while less common minerals, including most of the ores, are deposited in veins, cavities and pore spaces in the rocks by gases and solutions that have originated elsewhere.

Most ores are found where there has been some igneous activity, usually the intrusion of plutonic rocks into sediments. This means that ores are generally found in areas where the roots of ancient mountains have been exposed by millions of years of weathering. Many ores occur with specific igneous rocks, for instance ilmenite with gabbro, cassiterite and uraninite with granite and beryl in granite pegmatites.

As magma cools underground, the common elements combine to form silicates. If the right elements are present, ore minerals like magnetite, ilmenite or platinum will also crystallize from the melt. As these minerals are heavy they tend to sink and if enough of one mineral is formed it may settle out as a distinct layer or segregation at the base of the igneous rock.

As silicates crystallize they use up the common elements, and the rare elements become concentrated in the remaining liquid together with water vapour and other gases such as carbon dioxide, chlorine and fluorine. The gases rise through pores and joints in the surrounding rock and, if the magma is near the surface, they may be expelled during an eruption, or escape quietly from fumaroles or a dormant volcano. Minerals carried by these gases can be deposited directly, and fumaroles are often encrusted with minerals such as

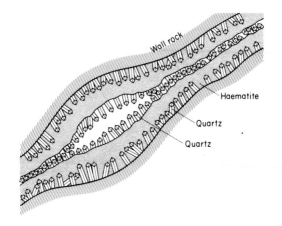

Mineral vein with a cavity or druse

sulphur. In the Valley of Ten Thousand Smokes in Alaska the fumaroles have deposits of magnetite, haematite, pyrite, galena, sphalerite, molybdenite and chalcopyrite.

If gases from magma do not reach the surface they may deposit the minerals they carry in the pores of overlying rocks or mix with groundwater and emerge as hot springs.

The remaining liquid fraction of the magma is very watery and contains the last silicates to crystallize: orthoclase quartz and micas; and the rare elements including those which make up minerals like tourmaline, beryl, uraninite, apatite and topaz. The water in the melt allows large crystals to grow, forming pegmatites which fill cavities, fractures and joints in and around the igneous rock.

As the pegmatite solidifies, water containing metallic sulphides and gangue minerals in solution is squeezed out and forced further into the country rock, cooling as it does so and forming hydrothermal mineral deposits. These may

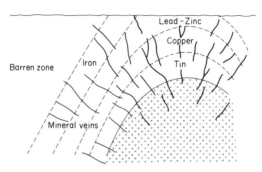

Temperature zoning of mineral veins around a granite intrusion

fill openings in breccias, joints, fissures and pore spaces in the rock, or the solutions may form veins by dissolving and replacing part of the rock. This is particularly common where the rock is limestone. Mineral veins usually contain separate layers of ore and gangue and if there has been more than one phase of mineralization there may be several layers. If the vein widens out into a cavity, called a druse, well shaped crystals will be able to grow and line the walls of the cavity.

Minerals are deposited from solution at different temperatures. High temperature ores are found in veins in and near an igneous rock and lower temperature minerals form further away from the intrusion. Veins may contain a single ore mineral or two or more minerals which crystallize at the same temperature. Common associations are gold and silver, silver and galena, galena sphalerite and chalcopyrite, chalcopyrite and pyrite, cassiterite and wolframite. Cassiterite is deposited at high temperatures, galena and sphalerite at intermediate and siderite and goethite at low temperatures.

Because of the zoning of hydrothermal minerals, a vein of galena followed toward a granite mass may yield chalcopyrite and then cassiterite. However, the minerals

34

associated with an igneous body depend on the elements present in the magma. Cassiterite for instance is found with only a certain few granites.

Sedimentary processes can help to concentrate minerals.

Weathering may break down a rock, and the ore minerals will then be washed away to be deposited at some distance from source as a placer deposit. A soluble mineral or one affected by the acid in rainwater can be dissolved from the upper part of a vein and redeposited at depth, in what is termed a zone of secondary enrichment. If this happens over a wide area, as it does for instance in some copper mining districts, it can cause a rock originally containing only a small percentage of the copper mineral to yield a very profitable ore.

Weathering can also create new materials such as kaolinite, which is formed by the decomposition of felspar in granite, and bauxite which is produced under wet tropical conditions. Iron oxide from the breakdown of mafic minerals can be deposited in lakes and swamps as bog iron ore.

Metamorphism also makes new minerals. Carbon-rich organic remains are altered to graphite, and magnesium-rich rocks to talc and serpentine.

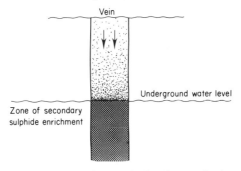

Secondary enrichment of a mineral vein; rainwater dissolves minerals near the surface and deposits them lower down

IDENTIFYING MINERALS

The appearance of a mineral, its shape and colour may be sufficient to identify it but as most minerals vary in colour and may take several different forms you will often have to check other properties of a specimen before deciding what it is.

Form Some minerals grow into crystals, the shape of which helps in their identification. The atomic structure controls the symmetry and overall shape of the crystals.

Crystals may be grouped together in seven systems based on their symmetry. Crystals may show one or more planes and/or axes of symmetry, and may have a centre of symmetry. Their differences are determined by axes and angles.

Cubic system (isometric and regular): all three axes have the same length and intersect at right angles.

Tetragonal: all three axes intersect at right angles; two are of the same length and in the same plane, while the third (the main axis) is either shorter or longer.

Rhombic system (orthorhombic): three axes of equal length are at right angles.

Monoclinic system: two of the three axes, all of which are unequal in length, are at right angles to each other with the third inclined.

Hexagonal system: three of four axes are in the same plane, are of equal length and intersect at the centre at intervals of 120°, giving 60° between each point of intersection. The fourth axis, of differing length, is at right angles to the others.

Trigonal system (rhombohedral): axes and angles are similar to the hexagonal system and often the two systems are combined as the hexagonal. The differences are those of symmetry. In the hexagonal system described above, the cross-section of the prism base is six-sided, whereas in the trigonal system it is three-sided. The hexagonal shape is formed when the corners of the triangles are bevelled.

Triclinic system: all three sides are of different lengths and inclined towards each other.

CRYSTAL FORMS

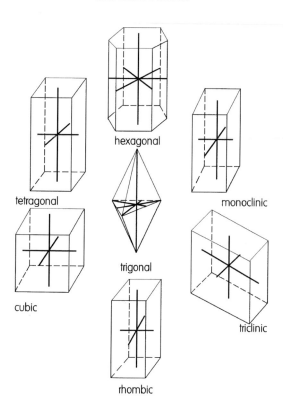

tetragonal

hexagonal

monoclinic

trigonal

cubic

triclinic

rhombic

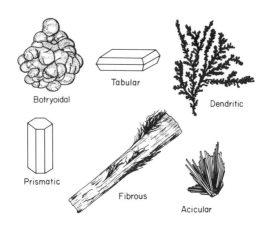

Botryoidal

Tabular

Dendritic

Prismatic

Fibrous

Acicular

HABIT OF CRYSTALS AND AGGREGATES

The word 'crystal' is derived from the Greek term *krystallos*, which means clear ice.

A crystal is a mineral with naturally occurring faces which are usually flat and meet along straight edges. Some crystals have such smooth mirrorlike faces and sharp edges that they look as if they have been cut by a jeweller. Minerals which in fact have been cut and polished are no longer crystals because their shape is man-made.

Each mineral is made of atoms arranged in a certain pattern and it is this internal atomic order that gives crystals of different minerals their characteristic shapes. Atoms are added to the pattern on all sides if this is physically possible, but usually some faces grow faster than others. The resulting crystal will thus not be perfect, but the internal symmetry will still be there.

Perfect crystals grow only under perfect conditions. If

growth is intermittent the crystal may show striations. These are straight lines on some of the faces which may run parallel to the length of the crystal or across it, and they may affect all or only some of the faces. The striations on a tourmaline crystal run along its length and those on a cube of pyrite are at right angles to striations on adjacent faces.

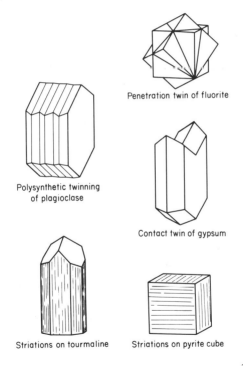

Penetration twin of fluorite

Polysynthetic twinning
of plagioclase

Contact twin of gypsum

Striations on tourmaline   Striations on pyrite cube

The direction of growth of a crystal may change, producing twin crystals. Contact twins are joined along one of their faces like the swallowtail twins of gypsum. Repeated contact twinning gives polysynthetic twins like those of plagioclase. Penetration twins appear to grow into one another like the twins of fluorite. In nature space is often limited and minerals are unable to grow freely; also the growing crystals interfere with each other, forming aggregates. Most aggregates are granular but sometimes the aggregate has a distinctive form which helps to identify it.

A few minerals, for instance opal and limonite, do not form crystals and these are said to be amorphous.

Cleavage The shape of a crystal is modified by the way it breaks. Some crystals break cleanly along certain planes because their atoms are held together less strongly in some directions than others. A straight-sided break resulting from this lack of cohesion is called cleavage. Cleavage can be seen as step-like breaks on the outside of a mineral or as cracks in a transparent one.

A mineral may have more than one cleavage direction. If it has three it may break into regular fragments as calcite breaks into rhombs. Diamonds cleave into octahedra and gem cutters use this property to remove flawed parts. A valuable diamond is studied for weeks to determine the cleavage planes and then with a sharp tap the cutter cleaves it in just the right place to produce a stone which when cut and polished will be a flawless gem.

Fracture In addition to cleavage, many minerals show an uneven kind of break called fracture. The most useful for identification is conchoidal fracture, which can be seen in quartz and resembles glass. Stone Age tools of flint or obsidian owe their shape to conchoidal fracture, which made it possible for men to chip off curved flakes and produce a sharp edge.

Colour The colour of a mineral is often its most striking feature but it can be confusing. The colour of cinnabar and

Cubic
cleavage

Octahedral
cleavage

Rhombohedral
cleavage

Basal or
platy cleavage

Conchoidal fracture

CLEAVAGE AND FRACTURE

malachite is a property of the mineral itself and therefore constant. This is also true of many minerals with metallic lustre. In the majority of non-metallic minerals however, the colour is due to very small amounts of some impurity, and the same mineral may thus have several colours. Corundum is colourless when pure but is often tinted red by traces of chromium or blue by titanium, and is then known as ruby or sapphire according to the colour.

Another colour effect occurs in some minerals which tarnish, and must be scratched to show the true colour underneath, like bornite.

Lustre The commonest type of lustre is vitreous, or glassy. Minerals with vitreous lustre are usually also transparent or translucent. Adamantine lustre is similar but much more brilliant, as in diamond. Metallic lustre is the typical sheen of metal possessed by sulphides like galena and pyrite. Minerals with metallic lustre are always opaque.

Minerals like mica, which have a very pronounced basal cleavage, often have pearly lustre due to the parallel layers

41

refracting light and breaking it up into tiny rainbows. Silky lustre is a characteristic of fibrous minerals like satinspar gypsum. The terms resinous and greasy lustre speak for themselves, and a mineral which is earthy or dull has no lustre at all.

Streak The colour of the powder of a mineral is known as its streak, and is obtained by rubbing the mineral on a piece of unglazed porcelain. Special streak plates can be purchased or you can use the back of a porcelain tile, or the broken edge of a piece of china. Streak is useful for identification because it shows the body colour of the mineral, not the colour given by impurities or tarnish. In many cases colour and streak are the same but most metallic minerals have a black or dark grey streak, even pyrite which is brassy gold in colour. Haematite, which looks dark grey when crystalline, has a brick-red streak.

Hardness A mineral may be very hard even though it may break easily. Hardness is its resistance to scratching and is judged by the minerals it scratches and those by which it is scratched. A series of minerals were arranged in order of hardness ranging from soft talc to diamond, the hardest natural substance, by F. Mohs in 1812. These are still used to test unknown minerals for hardness

RELATIVE AND ABSOLUTE HARDNESS SCALE

Mohs' hardness	Mineral
1	talc
2	gypsum
3	calcite
4	fluorite
5	apatite
6	orthoclase
7	quartz
8	topaz
9	corundum
10	diamond

When testing minerals the rule is that a mineral scratches those less hard than itself and is scratched by harder minerals. Two minerals of equal hardness scratch each other. A mineral made up of grains or fibres may appear softer than it should when scratched because the particles are forced apart. Examine test scratches with a lens and rub them to make sure they really are scratches. A soft mineral leaves a line of powder on a harder one which may look like a scratch, and a knife may leave a silver streak of metal on hard minerals.

Some crystals have different hardnesses in different directions. Kyanite has a hardness of $4\frac{1}{2}$ along its crystals but a hardness of 7 across them. Calcite usually has a hardness of 3 but in one direction has a hardness of 2 and is easily scratched by a finger-nail. It is a good idea to collect at least the first seven minerals of Mohs' Scale for hardness tests, but do not use your best specimens because they will soon be covered with scratches. Minerals with a hardness of 7 or more are rare so you are not likely to need gemstones for testing them.

A quick way of testing for hardness in the field is to rub the mineral on a fine steel file to see how much powder or noise it produces. Soft minerals produce much powder and little noise, hard minerals give little or no powder but make quite a loud noise. This test is useful as it also shows the streak of the mineral.

Absolute hardness	Simple testing devices
0.03	fingernail: rubbing with greasy feel
1.25	fingernail: scratching possible
4.50	copper coin: scratching possible
5.00	knife: scratching easily possible
6.50	knife: scratching still possible
37.00	steel file: scratching possible
120.00	will scratch window glass
175.00	
1,000.00	
140,000.00	

Specific Gravity   Also known as relative density. Some minerals are surprisingly heavy or light for their size. Specific gravity is the ratio of the weight of a body to that of an equal volume of water. The specific gravity of minerals varies between 1 and 20. Values under 2 are considered light (amber is 1.1); those from 2 to 4 normal (calcite is 2.7); and those above 4 heavy (lead is 7.5). Typical metallic minerals, such as pyrite (page 74) and haematite (page 77), have a specific gravity of about 5 (4.9–5.2 and 5.2–5.3 respectively), but typical non-metallic minerals have specific gravities of between 2.5 and 3.0.

With practice, the specific gravity of an unknown mineral can be estimated; where this departs from the normal range, it is likely to be on the high side. The relationship between colour and specific gravity can be helpful, as dark minerals are often relatively heavy and the light-coloured minerals often relatively light, and thus exceptions to the rule are fairly easy to identify.

Other Properties   Flakes of flexible minerals such as chlorite can be bent between the fingers and stay bent. Elastic crystals like the micas can be bent too but will spring back unless bent so far that they begin to fracture. A malleable mineral, like gold, can be beaten into flat sheets without breaking. Ductile minerals can be drawn out into wires without breaking. Sectile minerals such as gypsum can be cut with a knife although they crumble when hammered. Some metals show all of the last three named properties.

Magnetic minerals like magnetite and pyrrhotite, when held near a compass, will deflect the needle. Easily fusible minerals such as stibnite and sulphur melt at comparatively low temperatures.

Some minerals fizz when dilute acid touches them. Carbonates like calcite and malachite react with the acid to form carbon dioxide, which is given off as bubbles. Dilute hydrochloric acid is usually used for this test but vinegar (acetic acid) is almost as good. The powdered mineral may react if the solid does not and the reaction can be speeded up by warming the acid.

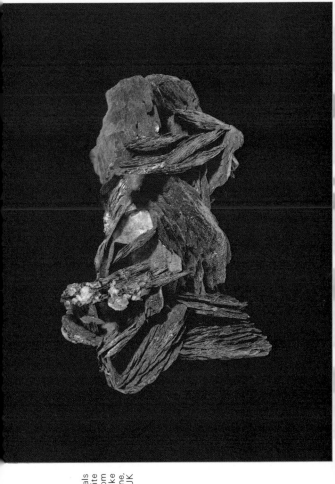

Platy crystals of torbernite from Gunnislake mine, Cornwall, UK

DESCRIPTIONS OF MINERALS

The entries are headed in bold type with the mineral name that is accepted by the scientific authorities; and a chemical description is given in italic. Any additional names are given in brackets, including miners' names, local names and variety names.

Uraninite (Pitchblende) *Uranium oxide* (UO_2)   Crystals of uraninite are rare but when found may be cubes, octahedra or dodecahedra. Usually uraninite occurs as botryoidal or massive pitchblende. It is a brownish black, black or grey opaque mineral with a typically greasy or pitchlike lustre but it is sometimes metallic or dull. The streak is brownish black or grey, usually with a green tinge. The hardness is 4–6, the specific gravity of crystals is 7.5–10.6 and that of pitchblende, which is a mixture of uraninite and other uranium minerals, $6\frac{1}{2}$–$8\frac{1}{2}$.

Pitchblende is radioactive and if placed on a photographic film in the dark for 24 hours the radiation it emits leaves a trace on the film. This was first noticed in 1896 by the French physicist Becquerel and led Marie Curie, who was then a young research student, to study the phenomenon. She found that uranium minerals are far more radioactive than the uranium they contain, and after years of work she and her husband Pierre Curie isolated from pitchblende minute amounts of two new radioactive minerals, which were the source of the extra radiation. One of these, which they named radium, is used today as an x-ray source. Uranium minerals contain 320 mg of radium per tonne of uranium.

Radiation occurs because radioactive elements give off electrically charged particles as they decay through a series of elements into helium and lead. Uraninite contains small amounts of these end products and since we know how long it takes for uranium to decay, the ratio of uranium to lead gives the age of the mineral, and hence of the rock containing it. This method is useful for dating ancient rocks but is not very reliable for younger rocks, because uranium decays so slowly that the amount of lead produced is very small, and is difficult to measure accurately.

Uraninite can be distinguished by its heaviness, colour and greasy lustre but above all by its radioactivity. Lack of magnetism distinguishes uraninite from magnetite, and unlike cassiterite it has a dark streak.

Pure uraninite occurs in acid pegmatites associated with granite or syenite but pitchblende is a high temperature hydrothermal mineral deposited in veins around granites with cassiterite, pyrite, galena and silver. Extensive deposits occur in Ontario, Canada and Shaba, Zaire.

Uraninite is one of the world's most valuable ores, containing as it does both radium which can be used to cure cancer, and uranium, which is a source of atomic power.

Tobernite (Uran-mica) *Hydrous copper uranium phosphate* ($Cu[UO_2/PO_4]_2 \cdot 8-12H_2O$) Square prism crystals, usually short and tabular. Scaly aggregates are common, the platy cleavage giving thin mica-like scales but unlike those of mica the torbernite flakes are brittle. The colour varies from emerald to yellow-green. The crystals are transparent to translucent with a vitreous lustre, pearly on cleavage faces. The streak is pale green, the hardness $2-2\frac{1}{2}$, and specific gravity 3.3 increasing to 3.7 as it alters to similar looking metatorbernite. Torbernite is distinguished by the colour, radioactivity, the square outline of scales and crystals and its perfect basal cleavage.

Torbernite is a secondary mineral formed by the oxidation of uraninite in veins containing copper ores.

Galena (Lead glance, Blue lead) *Lead sulphide* (PbS) Crystals are common and are usually cubes which are often striated, but they are also found as octahedra and pyritohedra. Granular masses occur but can be identified by their perfect cubic cleavage and dark lead grey colour. Galena has a metallic lustre when fresh, but quickly oxidizes

Lead-grey crystals of galena with calcite on brown siderite from Neudorf, Harz Mountains, Germany

Acicular crystals of cerussite from Stanhope Burn mine, Co. Durham, UK

to a dull film on contact with air. It has a hardness of $2\frac{1}{2}$–3 and a grey-black streak which will mark paper. Its specific gravity is 7.2–7.6, which together with its cubic cleavage helps to distinguish it from stibnite and dark sphalerite.

Galena is often found with sphalerite, pyrite and chalcopyrite in hydrothermal veins with barytes, fluorite and calcite as gangue minerals. It also occurs as a replacement mineral in limestone cavities.

Galena is 86 per cent lead and is the chief ore of that metal, but usually contains in addition a small amount of silver, which is a valuable by-product of lead extraction. The leading lead producing areas include Broken Hill in Australia, the Tri-state mining district in the Mississippi valley, and Leadville, Colorado. Saint Eulalia, Mexico has galena deposits which are extremely rich in silver.

Lead is still occasionally used for pipes as it was in the time of the Romans. Some buildings, notably churches, have lead covered roofs and lead is used for making solder, pewter, bullets and lead shot. It is used to make car batteries, rust proof paint, and shielding for radioactive sources.

Cerussite (White lead) *Lead carbonate* ($PbCO_3$) Prismatic or acicular crystals are common and these often occur in radiating masses. They are usually white or transparent to translucent, with an adamantine lustre and a conchoidal fracture. The streak is white, the hardness is 3 to $3\frac{1}{2}$ and the specific gravity is 6.4–6.6, a heaviness that distinguishes cerussite from all other white minerals except anglesite, the sulphate of lead.

Anglesite and cerussite are weathering products of galena and are usually found with it in the upper parts of lead ore veins. They are both ores of lead when found in worthwhile quantities, as in Mexico. Lead carbonate is also used as a pigment and the colours known as Venetian White and Dutch White are mixtures of basic lead carbonate and ground barytes.

The Roman emperor Nero and his wife Poppaea used white lead mixed with chalk to improve their complexions, and a similar face powder was used by both ladies and gentlemen in the eighteenth century; a very dangerous fashion, since lead is a poison which slowly accumulates in the body until the concentration becomes fatal.

Mercury (Quicksilver) (Hg)   Native mercury is rare and has the distinction of being the only liquid mineral apart from water. It is deposited with cinnabar in volcanic areas as tiny globules in rocks or small pools in cavities. It is a shining opaque liquid with a mirror-like surface, metallic lustre and a specific gravity of 13.6. It has been known for thousands of years and a bead of mercury was found in an amulet from an Egyptian tomb dating from the fifteenth or sixteenth century BC. Liquid solidifies at $-38.9°C$.

Amalgam   Amalgams are alloys formed when mercury dissolves other metals, especially gold or silver. A natural silver amalgam appears as tiny marbles, grains or flakes. It always accompanies drops of mercury as they develop jointly from the wearing of cinnabar. The main silver amalgam deposits are in Bavaria and Chile, and a natural gold amalgam is in Columbia.

The amalgam method has been used for more than two thousand years to extract gold and silver from their ores. Mercury dissolves the gold or silver and then the amalgam is heated to vaporize the mercury which can then be condensed and used again. Artificially made amalgams are used for filling teeth. Its specific gravity is 12–13.

Cinnabar *Mercuric sulphide* (HgS)   Cinnabar crystals may be acicular or short prisms and are translucent to opaque with an adamantine lustre. The more common massive or earthy form is dull, though sometimes under a lens minute cleavage planes can be seen twinkling as they reflect the light. Cinnabar varies from vermilion to dark red and may even be black when impure, but its streak is bright red. Its hardness is 2 to $2\frac{1}{2}$ and the specific gravity is 8, which with the streak distinguishes cinnabar from other red minerals. It can alter to whitish grey calomel or tiny globules or native mercury.

Cinnabar is a low temperature hydrothermal mineral and

is deposited today around hot springs and in veins near recent volcanic rocks. Cinnabar is often found in low temperature quartz veins with stibnite. The largest crystals come from Hunan in China but the most extensive deposits are at Almaden in Spain, Idrija in Serbia, in California (especially) and Texas in the USA.

Cinnabar is 86 per cent mercury and is the principal ore of the metal. Powdered cinnabar or vermilion used to be a popular red pigment but is no longer used for vermilion paints, because like all mercury compounds it is poisonous. Mercury based fungicides used to dress seed corn can be fatal to wildlife and even to people who eat the corn by mistake.

Gold (Au) Gold has been prized since the beginning of civilization for its beauty, resistance to tarnish and the ease with which it can be worked. Because of its reluctance to react with other elements gold is found native, usually alloyed with a percentage of silver or copper. It forms cubic or octahedral crystals but they are extremely rare. Nuggets are also rare enough for large ones to be given names, such as the Welcome Stranger which was found in 1869 at Ballarat in Australia, and weighed 2280 oz.

Gold is usually found as flecks, grains or dendritic aggregates in quartz veins and some granites but the gold used by the earliest metal workers was placer gold. The colour varies with the purity from pale yellow electrum, an alloy with over twenty per cent silver, to red gold which contains a small amount of copper. The purest natural gold, averaging 99.91 per cent gold, comes from Great Boulder Mine near Kalgoorlie, Australia.

Gold has a hardness of $2\frac{1}{2}$ to 3 when pure, and is malleable, ductile and sectile. Its softness and golden streak distinguish it from minerals like pyrite, which is called fool's gold because it can so easily be mistaken for the more valuable mineral. A test which is easier on the teeth than the traditional method of biting is to try to cut the gold with a penknife. Pyrite is too hard and chalcopyrite crumbles.

Weight is another good test for gold. It has a specific

Translucent vermilion red cinnabar from Almaden, Spain

gravity of 15.5–19.3 depending on the purity, which is measured in carats. 24 carat gold is absolutely pure but too soft for many uses, so other metals are added, to make it harder and of course cheaper. Most wedding rings and good quality jewellery are made of 22 or 18 carat gold. Nine carat gold is also popular but in some countries cannot legally be described as gold.

The great gold rushes to the Klondyke, to California and to Australia were stimulated by the discovery of nuggets and dust in placer deposits but these were soon worked out and most of the gold produced in the world today is mined. Gold is sometimes deposited in quartz-pyrite veins associated with granites, usually as flecks too minute to be seen; and traces of gold are incorporated into pyrite and other sulphides. The greatest deposit is the Banket, a quartz conglomerate mined at the Witwatersrand in South Africa and producing 40 per cent of the annual world total. The Banket is thought to be a fossil placer deposit in which gold from ancient mountains was concentrated millions of years ago. Mines have been sunk in it to a depth of 3000 to 3500 m where the temperature is over 50°C, and only expensive refrigeration equipment makes mining possible.

Gold has always been used for jewellery, ornaments and objects of value but the first king to use gold as money was Croesus of Lydia, who issued gold staters around 560 BC.

Gold nugget from Ballinvalley, Co. Wicklow, Ireland

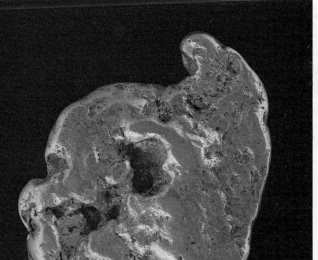

British gold was never abundant enough to be used for money; however in the Bronze Age enough was produced to make many torcs, the heavy neck rings worn by Celtic chiefs.

Gold's resistance to tarnish makes it ideal for microcircuits in electrical apparatus and for filling and crowning teeth. Organic gold solutions are given as injections to treat arthritis and a solution called Purple of Cassius is used to colour glass and ceramics red, blue and purple.

The high reflectivity of gold extends into the infra-red part of the spectrum, and a very thin layer of gold may thus be used to shield spacecraft against overheating. Buildings too are sometimes fitted with sun insulating windows, which are coated with a film of gold so thin that it is transparent, but is sufficient to reflect back much of the heat which would otherwise enter the building. Gold is also important for making solar cells, such as are carried by many spacecraft; the reflecting power of the gold is used in the cells to store the energy of the sunlight.

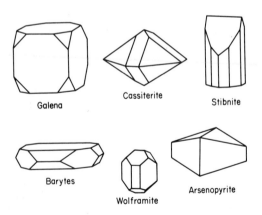

Galena

Cassiterite

Stibnite

Barytes

Wolframite

Arsenopyrite

Platinum (Pt)   It may be found native as grains or nuggets, sometimes alloyed with iron, copper, gold and the rare metals palladium, osmium, iridium, and rhodium. Platinum is a greyish-white lustrous metal with a hardness of $4-4\frac{1}{2}$ and a specific gravity when pure of 21.5, though when it occurs naturally its specific gravity is usually something between 14 and 19 because of the lighter metals alloyed with it. It is malleable and ductile and extremely resistant to corrosion. It may also be magnetic because of the iron it contains and some specimens from the Ural mountains in the USSR attract iron more powerfully than a magnet of similar size.

Platinum can be distinguished from gold by its colour, and from all other minerals by its weight. It occurs as disseminated grains in basic and ultrabasic rocks like peridotite and gabbro, and is usually found in placer deposits derived from such rocks. In the Urals a nugget weighing 11 kg was once found. Other sources are the Bushveld Complex in South Africa, Sudbury, Ontario, where platinum is a by-product of nickel extraction, Colombia and Alaska.

Platinum is used for jewellery. Its chemical inertness and high melting point also make it ideal for laboratory apparatus, standard lengths and weights and as a catalyst to speed up chemical reactions.

Wolframite *Iron manganese tungsten oxide* $(FeMn)WO_4$ It forms tabular prismatic or bladed crystals which are opaque and brown or grey-black with a sub-metallic lustre. Its streak may be reddish or dark brown and it has a hardness of $4\frac{1}{2}$ to $5\frac{1}{2}$. Wolframite can be recognized by its colour and specific gravity which is 7 to 7.5, and being heavy it is often found in placers with cassiterite, as in Cornwall, Bolivia, Burma and Malaysia. The wolframite in these deposits has weathered out of hydrothermal veins and pegmatites associated with granites. Minerals commonly found with it are cassiterite, topaz, tourmaline, and fluorite.

Wolframite used to be avoided by miners because it made the smelting of tin difficult but now it is valuable as the chief ore of tungsten.

Tungsten has the highest melting point of all metals and is used in engine valves, electric lamp filaments and special hard steel for toolmaking. Tungsten carbide is one of the hardest materials known and is used on drill bits for oilfields and rock drilling, and on the cutters of coalmining machines.

Wolframite is found in and around granites in high temperature hydrothermal veins and placers derived from them. The chief producers are China, the USA, Bolivia and South Korea.

Barite (barytes, Heavy spar) *Barium sulphate* ($BaSO_4$)   Crystals of barite are usually tabular, often found in clusters forming cockscomb barytes, or in granular masses. A concretionary variety is known as Bologna stone, and clusters of crystals enclosing sand are called desert roses. The colour is white, translucent to opaque with a vitreous or pearly lustre but the crystals are often tinted yellow, red, brown, and sometimes bluish green. The streak is white; the hardness is 3 to $3\frac{1}{2}$ and the specific gravity is 4.48, surprisingly heavy for a non-metallic mineral.

Barytes is usually found accompanying quartz and fluorite as the gangue in sphalerite and galena veins. In recent years, however, barytes has become important to the oil industry and old lead mines have been opened in some areas and worked for barytes. The mineral is also found as nodules in clays left by the weathering of some limestones. Barytes forms the cement in some sandstones like the Elgin sandstones of Scotland. The finest large crystals come from Cumbria, England and from Felsobanya in eastern Europe. Red brown desert roses are found at Norman, Oklahoma. Barite was used in the manufacture of asbestos goods; as barium sulphide it forms the base of white paint, and when ground it is used as a filler for paper. It absorbs gamma rays, and therefore special concrete and bricks are made with barytes for shielding radioactive sources in hospitals. The main use of the mineral is in heavy drilling mud for oil wells. Powdered barytes is forced down the drill hole to carry back rock cuttings and prevent water, gas or oil entering the hole before it is completed.

Platinum nuggets found in the Ural mountains near Sverdlovsk

Tabular crystals of barytes from Florence Mine, Cumbria, UK

Stibnite (Antimonite) *Antimony sulphide* (Sb$_2$S$_3$)   It is found in crystals which are prismatic or acicular and it frequently occurs in radiating aggregates. The crystals may be vertically striated and show perfect longitudinal cleavage, although sometimes they are bent or curved. Stibnite is a lead grey opaque mineral with a metallic lustre which may be obscured by a pale yellow tarnish. The hardness is 2; stibnite is sectile and will mark paper. The streak is lead grey. With a specific gravity of 4$\frac{1}{2}$, it is much lighter than similarly coloured galena, and is also distinguished by its cleavage and the fact that it will melt in a match flame.

Stibnite is a low temperature vein mineral often found with arsenic minerals, cinnabar, galena and sphalerite. Veins and pockets of massive stibnite are found in a brecciated sandstone in Hunan Province, China, one of the world's chief sources. There are also extensive deposits in Mexico. Good crystals come from Felsobanya in eastern Europe and Shikoku Island, Japan, where crystals up to a metre long have been found.

Stibnite contains up to 71 per cent antimony and is the chief ore of this metal, which is used to increase the hardness of certain alloys like type metal and pewter; it is also used in fireworks, medicines and vulcanized rubber. Stibnite crystals have been used since ancient times as eyebrow pencils or ground to a grey powder called *kohl* which was used by Arab and Chinese women centuries ago to darken their eyelids.

Cassiterite (Tinstone) *Tin Oxide* (SnO$_2$)   The crystals are prismatic or pyramidal and often form geniculate twins, but the mineral also occurs in massive form and as radiating fibres known as wood tin or toad's eye tin. Pure cassiterite would be colourless but it is usually coloured by iron and may be yellow or reddish brown to nearly black. Pale crystals are transparent and bands or zones of different shades of colour can be seen in them. Dark crystals are opaque. The crystals have a brilliant adamantine lustre but waterworn stream tin looks greasy. The hardness is 6 to 7 and the streak is very light, varying from white to grey or light brown. The specific gravity of cassiterite is 6.8 to 7.1 and this heaviness together with the streak and hardness help to identify it.

Cassiterite is a high temperature hydrothermal mineral found in and around some granites as in Cornwall, Saxony and Bolivia. Placer deposits of stream tin are worked in Malaysia, Thailand and Indonesia.

Cassiterite is the principal ore of tin and has been used for thousands of years to make bronze, an alloy of copper and tin which is far superior in hardness to copper alone.

The name comes from *kassiteros*, the Greek name for tin, and in the Bronze Age when the Phoenicians traded Cornish cassiterite all over the Mediterranean, Britain was called the *Cassiterides*, or tin islands.

Used today mainly for preserving food (cans and foil). A coating of tin (usually less than 0.0004 mm thick) is deposited on mild steel to prevent it from rusting. Tin is still used to make bronze, and other alloys including pewter, type metal and solder. It is also added to some toothpastes in the form of stannous fluoride, and used to add weight to silks and stabilize the perfume in soaps. Tin compounds are replacing poisonous organomercury in paper manufacture, and they are used as a wood preservative and as a fungicide for potatoes.

Silver (Ag)   Native silver may be cubic or octahedral but is more often dendritic or wiry. It is nearly always covered with black silver sulphide and this tarnish makes it difficult to recognize. Its colour when fresh is metallic white with a shining silver streak, but it may be pale yellow if it contains some gold or copper. Silver is heavy and has a specific gravity of 9.6–12 when pure. Gold or copper dissolved in it causes variations in weight. It is sectile, with a hardness of between $2\frac{1}{2}$ and 3. Silver is ductile and next to gold is the most malleable metal. This and its colour and tarnish help to identify silver.

Silver rarely forms nuggets like gold or platinum so it is usually found in veins, not placers. It is a late stage hydrothermal mineral and accompanies minerals like

Above: prismatic crystals of stibnite from Hungary, showing
longitudinal striations

Right: dendritic growth of native silver from Huantajaya
mines, Chile

Crystals of cassiterite from Saxony showing adamantine lustre, and worn pebbles of stream tin from placer deposits in New South Wales

argentite, galena, sphalerite, copper and gold. In the Lake Superior area in Canada the native silver fills the vesicles in a lava, and at Keeweenaw in Michigan it is intergrown with copper in masses called halfbreeds. The best crystals come from Kongsberg in Norway, where silver occurs in hydrothermal veins with argentite. Other well known deposits are the Comstock Lode in Nevada, Broken Hill in Australia, Peru, Chile and Freiberg, Germany.

In ancient Egypt silver was called the white gold. It was thought to be rarer than gold and was therefore more valuable, whereas today silver has about one twentieth of the value of gold. The name white gold is used today for an artificial alloy of gold, nickel, copper and zinc.

Silver is used in coins, jewellery, expensive cutlery and silver plate. Silver salts are used in medicine, for glass colouring and formed the basis of photographic processing.

Argentite (Silver glance) *Silver sulphide* (Ag_2S) This is common in veins with native silver which it usually covers with a black crust. Sometimes it is found in rough cubes or octahedra which are so distorted they are difficult to recognize. The colour when fresh is dark lead grey with a metallic lustre and shining streak, but exposed surfaces are dull black like tarnished silver. Argentite has a hardness of 2 to $2\frac{1}{2}$ and is so sectile it can be cut into shavings. This distinguishes argentite from galena which it resembles in colour and weight. Its specific gravity is 7.2–7.4.

Argentite is found in fairly low temperature hydrothermal veins, often with galena, sphalerite, pyrite and copper ores. It is 87 per cent silver and is the chief source of the metal. Much of the argentite produced today is a by product of galena and sphalerite mining as at Broken Hill Australia, or of cobalt and nickel production, as at Cobalt, Ontario. Large masses occur in the gold-bearing quartz veins of the Comstock Lode in Nevada, and in the silver mines at Potosí in Bolivia.

Molybdenite *Molybdenum sulphide* (MoS_2) This is usually found as flakes or scaly masses, but it occasionally occurs as tabular hexagonal crystals with a platy cleavage. The mineral is sectile and has a hardness of $1\frac{1}{2}$. It will mark paper and the streak on glazed porcelain or a fingernail has a greenish tinge. Molybdenite is steel grey or bluish with a metallic lustre and a greasy feel. It is heavier than graphite, with a specific gravity of 4.7 and can be distinguished from it also by its lighter colour and greenish streak. Molybdenite is the chief source of molybdenum which is used as an alloy with steel and an additive in lubricating oils.

Molybdenite is common but seldom found in quantities large enough to mine. The greatest concentration in the world is at Climax, Colorado, in thin veins which criss-cross the altered granite of Bartlett Mountain. It is usually found with granites in high temperature quartz veins with cassiterite and wolframite, as in Cornwall. In Mexico and Chile small amounts are produced as a by-product from copper ores.

Arsenopyrite (Mispickel, Poisonous pyrite) *Iron arsenic sulphide* (FeAsS) Arsenopyrite is one of the few minerals recognizable by its smell. When struck by a hammer, it gives off sparks and an odour resembling that of garlic.

Crystals are common, and are often found with striated faces. They are sometimes yellow enough to be confused with pyrite, although when fresh arsenopyrite is a metallic silvery white. The streak is a dark greyish black and the hardness is 5–6, softer than pyrite; specific gravity 5.9–6.2.

Arsenopyrite is found in high temperature hydrothermal veins with cassiterite, wolframite, silver, gold and sulphide minerals such as pyrite, chalcopyrite and galena. Arsenic is thus obtained as a by-product of tin, tungsten, silver and gold, and is recovered from the flue dust of smelters. It is used in medicines, paints and pesticides. Arsenic has been used for centuries as a poison, and as it can be absorbed through the skin arsenopyrite should be handled as little as possible.

Sphalerite (Blende, Zinc blende, Black jack, Ruby jack, Resin jack) *Zinc sulphide* (ZnS) Sphalerite occurs in a variety

Native copper from Mufulira mine, Zambia

Platy crystals of molybdenite from Raade, Norway

of colours, and even experts do not always recognize it. Usually sphalerite is granular, with a resinous lustre, though this may be adamantine or, in iron-rich specimens, almost metallic. It can be transparent, translucent or opaque, and has a hardness of $3\frac{1}{2}$–4, which distinguishes it from cassiterite. The streak is a light brown yellow or white, unlike silver ore or galena. Sphalerite is heavier than siderite. The most common colours are brown, black and yellow but red, green and almost colourless sphalerite occur.

It is found in hydrothermal veins with galena, pyrite and sometimes chalcopyrite. Large deposits are mined at Broken Hill in Australia; Leadville in Colorado and the Tri-state mining area in the Mississippi valley. There is usually some sphalerite wherever hydrothermal minerals occur.

Sphalerite is the main ore of zinc, but was not mined in any quantity until brass was invented in the sixteenth century. Its chief use is for galvanizing to iron to prevent it from rusting, and in alloys such as brass. Some toothpaste tubes are made of zinc. Zinc oxide and zinc sulphide are used in paints in place of poisonous white lead. Other zinc salts are used in dyes and glue, and in wood preservatives. Sphalerite is the chief source of the rare metals gallium, indium and germanium, which occur as impurities in the sphalerite and are recovered when the ore is smelted for zinc.

Copper (Cu) Copper is one of the few metals which can be found native, although even in the case of copper this is seldom in large amounts. The only site of any importance where native copper is mined is the Keeweenaw Peninsula, Lake Superior where it has been mined since prehistoric times. Copper is found there in conglomerates and in cavities and vesicles in ancient lavas. In some cases it is intergrown with silver, and sometimes it occurs in masses weighing many tons.

As well as forming irregular masses, copper is often dendritic or wiry, the branches made up of distorted cubic or octahedral crystals. It can be recognized by its metallic copper colour but, as it is often coated with malachite or

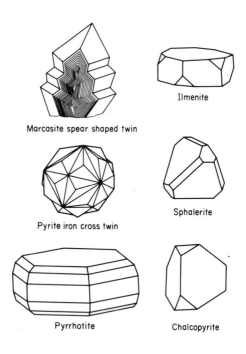

Marcasite spear shaped twin

Ilmenite

Pyrite iron cross twin

Sphalerite

Pyrrhotite

Chalcopyrite

azurite, or a dull brown tarnish, one has to scratch or break it before the true colour can be seen. Copper is malleable and ductile, and has a hardness of $2\frac{1}{2}$–3 so it is easily scratched. The streak is metallic and copper pink. Copper is heavy, with a specific gravity of 8.9. It is too easily weathered to form placer deposits.

Silver is the only metal which conducts electricity better than copper, but it is too expensive to use so electric wires and cables are made of copper. Copper is also used in alloys such as brass, gunmetal, bronze, and in 'copper' coins, which in fact contain comparatively little copper. Copper was the first metal to be used for toolmaking by early civilizations but was soon superseded by the much harder bronze, an alloy of copper and tin.

Chalcopyrite (Copper pyrites, Peacock copper) *Copper iron sulphide* ($CuFe_2S_3$) This is more often granular than crystalline and has a characteristic green, pink and purple iridescent coating which won for it the miners' name of peacock copper. It is brassy gold under the tarnish, a deeper colour than pyrite, and has a greenish black streak. Chalcopyrite has a hardness of $3\frac{1}{2}$–4 and this helps to distinguish it from pyrite, with which it often occurs. It is also lighter than pyrite with a specific gravity of 4.2, and it does not give a spark when struck with a hammer. The tarnish is similar to that of bornite but a scratch reveals the difference in the colour of the mineral underneath.

Chalcopyrite is usually a hydrothermal vein mineral found with other copper minerals and with pyrite, sphalerite and galena. It is also common in pegmatites and other igneous rocks and in contact metamorphosed limestones as at Bisbee, Arizona. It has a copper content of 34 per cent. It is the most abundant copper mineral and the principal ore of copper, and is found in most of the 'porphyry coppers', the diorite porphyry ore bodies in the south western USA and Chile. Chalcopyrite and pyrite are found together in many deposits, including those at Rio Tinto in Spain which have been mined for three thousand years, first for gold and later for copper.

Bornite (Erubescite, Peacock ore, Horseflesh ore) *Copper iron sulphide* ($Cu_5Fe_2S_4$) Rarely forms crystals and usually occurs as flecks in the rock or in granular masses. It is opaque with a metallic lustre and a dark grey streak, and tarnishes to a purplish iridescence which hides the copper pink colour. Bornite has a hardness of 3 so it can be scratched with a knife, and is also slightly sectile; its specific gravity is 4.9–5.4.

Massive chalcopyrite is easily confused with bornite as both develop an iridescent tarnish which gives rise to the miners' term 'peacock ore'; but if the tarnish is scratched, the brassy gold of chalcopyrite is quite different from the pinkish brown of bornite. Bornite is also called purple copper ore and horseflesh ore, both names referring to the colour. It is an important ore of copper at Mount Lyell in Tasmania and at Butte, Montana where it is found in veins with pyrite and chalcopyrite.

Bornite is also found in pegmatites and in the metamorphosed rocks close to igneous intrusions.

Chalcopyrite from Bourg d'Oisans, France, showing the typical iridescent tarnish which earned it the miners' name of Peacock Copper

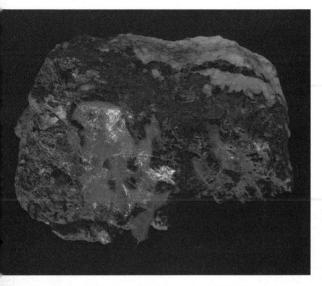

Cuprite from Fowey Consols mine, Cornwall: translucent red fibrous crystals forming the variety known as chalcotrichite

Covellite (Covelline) *Copper sulphide* (CuS)   A deep indigo blue mineral with a metallic lustre, it is often found with other copper minerals. It forms hexagonal platy crystals often standing on edge but it is usually massive. It is sometimes coated with chalcopyrite, which alters to covellite in the zone of secondary enrichment of ore veins.

Covellite has a hardness of $1\frac{1}{2}$–2. It is sectile and also marks paper; the streak is blue-black. It cleaves into thin hexagonal plates which are flexible but not elastic and this distinguishes covellite from other blue minerals. The blue colour turns to purple when wet and the mineral often has a black, purple or iridescent tarnish. The best crystals come from Calabana mine in Sardinia and Butte, Montana, which has been called the richest hill on earth. Specific gravity 4.68.

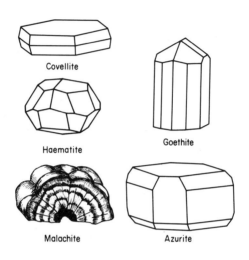

Covellite

Haematite

Goethite

Malachite

Azurite

Chalcocite (Redruthite, Chalcosine, Copper glance) *Copper sulphide with more copper than sulphur* (Cu_2S) An important copper ore that is usually massive rather than crystalline. It is a lead-grey to black metallic mineral with a dull black tarnish, often with blue or green spots. The streak is grey and chalcocite is moderately sectile with a hardness of $2\frac{1}{2}$–3. Chalcocite is less sectile than argentite (silver glance) and its colour and hardness distinguish it from other minerals. Its specific gravity is 5.5–5.8.

The various names are derived from *chalkos*, the Greek for copper, and from Redruth in Cornwall where chalcocite has been mined. Glance means a soft dark metallic sulphide.

Chalcocite is found with other copper minerals in the zone of enrichment of ore veins in many mining areas including Cornwall, Kongsberg in Norway and Butte, Montana. It is one of the minerals in the porphyry copper ores of Arizona, Utah and Nevada. In Oklahoma chalcocite forms nodules in sandstone; at Kennecott in Alaska pure masses of tens of thousands of tons occur.

Cuprite (Chalcotrichite, Red copper ore, Ruby copper) *Copper oxide* (Cu_2O)   This is produced by the oxidation of the other copper ores so it is only found in near surface veins, not deep underground. Usually granular or earthy, cuprite sometimes forms small crystals which are dark red or reddish black, translucent to opaque with adamantine to metallic lustre. Crystals can be cubes or octahedra but a variety called chalcotrichite is made of interlacing acicular or fibrous crystals. The crystals have a hardness of $3\frac{1}{2}$–4, a brownish red streak and conchoidal fracture. The streak distinguishes cuprite from similar looking cinnabar, and haematite is harder. The name comes from *cuprum*, the Latin for copper. Cuprite contains 88 per cent copper and is the richest ore of the metal apart from native copper itself. It alters to malachite and azurite and often occurs with them, as at Broken Hill in Australia, Katanga in Zaire, and Chile. Good crystals have been found in Cornwall and at Chessy in France. The specific gravity of cuprite is 5.6–6.2.

Malachite (Velvet ore, Satin ore, Rock green) *Hydrous copper carbonate* ($Cu_2CO_3[OH]_2$)   A semi-precious stone and also a valuable copper ore. It is commonly produced by the weathering of other copper minerals and is responsible for the green colour of tarnished copper or bronze. Malachite is easily recognized by its colour and green streak. The banded botryoidal form is distinctive. It also forms silky crusts of acicular crystals. The crystals are translucent and have a silky or velvety lustre; films and coatings of malachite are dull. Being a carbonate, malachite reacts with acid to produce bubbles of carbon dioxide. It has a hardness and specific gravity of 4, hard enough to resist wear but comparatively easy to shape and polish.

Deposits of malachite have been mined in the Urals and Siberia. The copper belt of Zambia and Zaire is one of the world's major sources of malachite, and large masses have

Globular aggregates of azurite with acicular green malachite from Bisbee, Arizona

been mined in South Australia. It occurs wherever there are copper deposits, especially in limestone areas.

Azurite (Chessylite) *Hydrous copper carbonate* ($Cu[OHCO_3]_2$)
A deep azure blue mineral that has a light blue streak, azurite forms velvety masses and rosettes of needle like crystals or tabular aggregates with a vitreous to adamantine lustre and conchoidal fracture. Azurite also occurs in opaque earthy masses. It has a hardness of $3\frac{1}{2}$–4 and a specific gravity of between 3.7 and 3.9, and it effervesces with acid. Similar blue minerals are harder and do not react with acid.

Azurite is 55 per cent copper and in Arizona and South Australia large masses have been worked as an ore of copper. Azurite and malachite are useful prospecting guides as they are formed from other copper minerals by weathering, and can be seen as stains on ore-bearing rocks. Azurite is the rarer of the two and is altered to malachite by weathering.

In the fifteenth and sixteenth centuries ground azurite

Brassy gold octahedral pyrite crystals with colourless quartz from Butte, Montana, USA

was the most popular blue pigment among European artists but it is not very reliable, turning green as it gradually alters to malachite.

Pyrite (Iron pyrites, Fool's gold) *Iron sulphide* (FeS$_2$)   The commonest sulphide mineral and the one most often mistaken for gold. Its brassy colour resembles gold especially when it occurs as flecks or granular masses in rocks, but a piece large enough to test is easily distinguished from gold by its greenish black streak and hardness of 6–6½ which means that it can be scratched only by good quality steel. Pyrite crystals may be cubes, octahedra or pyritohedra, or combinations of these forms. They are often striated and are opaque with a metallic lustre. The specific gravity of pyrite is 5, which is average for a metallic mineral, but much lighter than gold. It is a lighter colour than chalcopyrite and unlike pyrrhotite is not magnetic. It is hard to distinguish from marcasite, which when freshly broken is a pale yellow, almost silvery colour but tarnishes very quickly.

Pyrite in a collection tends to decompose, and in museums where pyritized fossils are kept, precautions have to be taken to prevent them from disintegrating. A fossil which has survived for millions of years embedded in rock can crumble in a few months once it is exposed to air.

Pyrite can be found in igneous rocks, in coal, as cubes in slates like those of North Wales, and as nodules in blue or grey clays like the Gault Clay of south-east England and the Alum Shale of Sweden. Many of the fossils in these clays have been replaced by pyrite. Large deposits used to be mined as a poor iron ore and a source of sulphur, but mining pyrite is only really worthwhile if it contains a little gold or copper. At Rio Tinto in Spain large lenses of pyrite are found in low temperature hydrothermal veins with calcite, barytes and quartz gangue minerals.

Pyrite emits sparks when struck and has been used as a fire-making stone since prehistoric times. More recently it was used instead of flint in wheel-lock firearms, in which a steel wheel revolved against a piece of pyrite, throwing sparks into the pan where they ignited gunpowder.

Marcasite (White iron pyrites) *Iron sulphide* (FeS$_2$)   It is very similar to pyrite but forms at lower temperatures and is most common in limestones, especially chalk, and clays. Marcasite nodules, which are sometimes mistaken for meteorites, are made up of radiating acicular crystals. Spear shaped twins are also characteristic, and those found at Dover are often thought to be relics of Roman weapons. Fossils can be replaced by marcasite, and in collections they decay very rapidly. The specific gravity of marcasite is 4.5–4.9.

When cleaned with acid, marcasite is a silvery colour but it soon tarnishes. When found it is usually a brassy yellow, possibly a shade lighter than pyrite. The hardness of 6–6$\frac{1}{2}$ distinguishes it from other silvery minerals, but the twin crystals are the most distinctive feature. Marcasite has been used for the same purposes as pyrite, but in addition it can be made into jewellery, although it has to be coated with something to prevent it from tarnishing.

Pyrrhotite (Pyrrhotine, Magnetic iron pyrites) *Iron sulphide* (FeS)   This contains more sulphur than pyrite does and this gives it different properties. It is usually massive but sometimes tabular hexagonal crystals occur. A metallic bronze colour with a greyish black streak, it is lighter in weight than pyrite, with a specific gravity of 4.6. It is also softer with a hardness of 3$\frac{1}{2}$–4$\frac{1}{2}$. Pyrrhotite's best known distinguishing feature is its magnetism which varies in intensity but is always detectable in the powder. Like pyrite, it tends to crumble on exposure to air.

Pyrrhotite is found in pegmatites and hydrothermal deposits, and as a segregation deposit of basic igneous rocks. It often contains nickel and is mined as an important ore of that metal at Sudbury, Ontario. Meteorites contain a non-magnetic variety called troilite.

Magnetite (Lodestone, Black iron ore) *Iron oxide* (Fe$_3$O$_4$)   Occurs either as granular masses or crystals, especially in igneous rocks, and in sands derived from them. The crystals are often octahedral and sometimes have triangular striations on the faces. They are iron black and opaque, with a metallic

Striated pyrrhotite from Morro Velho, Brazil

lustre and black streak. Their hardness is $5\frac{1}{2}$–$6\frac{1}{2}$ and the specific gravity is 5.2.

Magnetite is 72.4 per cent iron and is strongly attracted by a magnet, a property weakly shown by many iron bearing minerals. In addition, the mineral can itself act as a magnet. The usual test for magnetism is to wave the specimen near a compass needle, which moves if the mineral is magnetic. In magnetite the degree of magnetism varies, and some specimens are magnetic enough to pick up iron. Natural magnets like this are called lodestones; when they are allowed to swing freely they point towards the North Pole. Lodestone was carried by ships to remagnetize their compass needles until the eighteenth century.

Magnetite was named after the shepherd Magnes who, tending his sheep on Mount Ida in Crete, suddenly found himself unable to move because the nails in his sandals and the ferrule of his staff stuck to the rock on which he was standing, which happened to be magnetite. Well known localities for lodestone in classical times were Monte

Calamita in Elba and Calabria in Spain. Today lodestone can be found in the Ural, Altai and Harz mountains and at Magnet Cove in Arkansas. Ordinary magnetite is common in placer deposits and most black beach sands are made of it. Magnetite is found with corundum in emery deposits, and in layers formed by segregation in igneous rocks as in the Bushveld Complex in South Africa and the Kiruna iron ore in Sweden. Magnetite is one of the richest and most abundant ores of iron.

Haematite (Looking glass ore, Red ochre, Paint rock, Kidney ore) *Iron oxide* (Fe_2O_3)   This is a heavy opaque red or red-brown mineral which gets its name from *haem*, the Greek word for blood. At $5\frac{1}{2}$–$6\frac{1}{2}$ hardness it will scratch

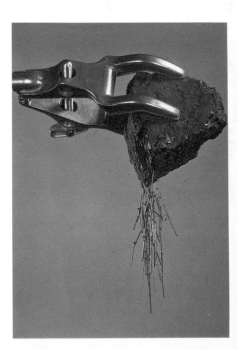

Magnetite
(lodestone)
showing its
magnetic
property

glass but is in turn scratched by quartz. It can be identified by this and by its streak, which is the colour of dried blood.

Specular haematite, or looking glass ore, is dark grey or black and forms platy or rhombohedral crystals. These have a brilliant metallic lustre and are used as intaglios in men's signet rings. The best sources of haematite for this purpose are Cumbria in England and the island of Elba. Elba and St Gotthard in Switzerland also produce unusual aggregates called iron roses.

Kidney ore occurs as metallic black or red-brown kidney shaped masses which when broken show radiating fibrous dark grey or brick red crystals. It is a valuable ore of iron. In Britain it is found in the limestones of the Forest of Dean and at Barrow-in-Furness, where haematite has replaced some of the limestone. The world's most productive iron mines, around Lake Superior in North America, obtain their ore from vast deposits of haematite interbedded with chert.

Red haematite is the cement in some sandstones, and may be found in mineral veins as a coating on crystals of quartz and calcite. Red ochre is a red earthy variety of haematite which is used as a pigment in paints and crayons and for polishing glass. It was used by prehistoric artists in their cave paintings.

Goethite (Brown haematite) *Hydrous iron oxide* (FeOOH) It is distinguished from limonite by the fact that it is crystalline, but it is very variable in form and visible crystals are uncommon. The crystals are brownish-black prisms with vertical striations, a metallic to adamantine lustre and a hardness of $5-5\frac{1}{2}$. It also occurs in velvety masses of yellow-brown acicular crystals. Goethite is often found as botryoidal aggregates and stalactites which when broken show radiating fibres or flat plates. They look like haematite but can be identified by their yellow-brown streak. Most yellow-brown goethite is earthy or oolitic and was thought to be limonite until x-ray examination revealed its crystalline structure. The specific gravity of goethite is 3.8–4.3.

Goethite is a late stage hydrothermal mineral found in veins with haematite, fluorite and barytes. It also occurs in cavities in limonite and is formed by the weathering of other iron minerals such as pyrite, magnetite and siderite, and is precipitated as 'bog iron ore' in lakes and marshes by the activity of iron-depositing bacteria.

Goethite is the most important iron ore after haematite as it is easily smelted and contains 63 per cent iron.

The mineral was named after the German poet and philosopher Goethe, who collected minerals.

Limonite (Yellow ochre) *Amorphous goethite* ($FeOOH+ nH_2O$) This is really natural rust, responsible for the yellow-brown colour of many soils and rocks. It is one of the oldest pigments, used to make prehistoric cave paintings and still used today as yellow ochre. It is amorphous and forms earthy masses, ooliths, nodules, stalactites and botryoidal crusts, but unlike goethite these do not show crystal structure when broken open. Limonite is usually dull brown or yellow but stalactites often have a dark glazed coating with a metallic lustre. The hardness and streak are the same as those of goethite, but earthy varieties are softer.

Limonite is used as an iron ore and makes up much of the oolitic Minette ores of Lorraine and Luxembourg and part of the Jurassic iron ore of England. In Cuba there are rich deposits in laterite soils formed by the weathering of serpentine. Hardness $4-5\frac{1}{2}$, specific gravity 2.7–4.3.

Siderite (Chalybite, Spathose iron) *Iron carbonate* ($FeCO_3$) It resembles the carbonates calcite and dolomite but is not at all like the other iron ores which are opaque and brightly coloured or metallic. It forms rhombohedral or scalenohedral crystals, transparent to translucent, and coloured brown, white, grey or pale yellow, with a vitreous to pearly lustre. The rhombohedral crystals usually have curved faces.

Siderite is brittle, with rhombohedral cleavage. It has a hardness of $4-4\frac{1}{2}$ so it can be scratched with a knife. The streak is white. The crystals often have a brown coating which, with the surprising weight, suggests iron. The specific gravity of 3.7 to 3.9 approaches that of barytes, but barytes is softer and has a different crystal form. Siderite

Limonite: a specimen of Northamptonshire ironstone showing the ochre yellow colour

Botryoidal haematite or Kidney Ore from Cumbria, UK

Dendritic pyrolusite on a rock is often mistaken for fossil plants

reacts with acid only if it is heated, and then, like other carbonates, it produces bubbles of carbon dioxide. On heating it becomes strongly magnetic and turns black.

Siderite is a low temperature hydrothermal mineral found with calcite, barytes and various sulphides. Concretionary masses called clay ironstone form in sedimentary rocks like the coal shales of Britain and Pennsylvania, where it is mined as an ore of iron. It is also formed as a result of the replacement of limestones by iron bearing solutions, and at Bilbao in Spain this type of deposit is an important iron ore. Oolitic ironstones like the Cleveland iron ore consist mainly of siderite which has replaced the calcite of the original ooliths.

The name come from *sideros*, which is Greek for iron.

Pyrolusite *Manganese oxide* (MnO_2) A very common manganese mineral, pyrolusite is black or steel-grey, and opaque; it has a black or bluish streak. It is usually massive with a dull earthy lustre but is also found as radiating fibres which have a metallic lustre. Dendritic aggregates resembling plants occur on the joints and bedding planes of sedimentary rocks and are often mistaken for fossils. In rough form pyrolusite has a hardness of 2–6 and will soil the fingers or mark paper, but crystals, which are rare, have a hardness of 6–7. The specific gravity varies from 4.5–5.

Pyrolusite is commonly formed under low temperature oxidizing conditions, as in quartz veins, and is precipitated from water at normal temperatures. A black deposit on boulders in a mountain stream, if it is sooty rather than slimy, is probably manganese oxide. Pyrolusite is also deposited with iron oxide as ferromanganese nodules on the sea floor. It has been estimated that 10 per cent of the area of the floor of the Pacific Ocean is covered with these nodules, so that they would be of considerable economic importance if a way could be found to collect them.

Pyrolusite is an important ore of manganese, the CIS and India being the chief producers. Manganese is used for making special steel alloys, dry batteries and permanganates for use as disinfectants. Pyrolusite itself has been used as a drier in paints and varnishes and to remove the colour caused by iron oxide in impure glass.

Ilmenite *Iron titanium oxide* ($FeTiO_3$) A black, opaque, metallic mineral, which forms tabular crystals but is also found as grains, flakes or in compact masses. It used to be mined as a low grade iron ore and the titanium it contained was an unwanted impurity, but ilmenite is now in demand as an ore of titanium.

Ilmenite crystals resemble those of haematite, but the mineral can be distinguished by its black streak. It has a hardness of 5–6, a specific gravity of 4.5–5 and is non-magnetic or very weakly magnetic, a property used to separate it from magnetite, with which it is often found.

Ilmenite occurs in basic igneous rocks and in placers derived from them. Ilmenite with magnetite is mined in the Adirondacks of New York State and in Egersund, Norway. Near Allard Lake, Quebec there are deposits of ilmenite with haematite. At Travancore in India a beach 23.37 km (17 miles) long is made of black sand of 70 per cent ilmenite. Similar black beach sands are mined in Australia and Florida.

Titanium is used in special steels and titanium white pigment in paints. It is also a component of the white smoke used for skywriting.

A block of Iceland Spar showing double refraction

Scalenohedral crystals of calcite from Cumbria, UK

Calcite (Calc spar, Iceland spar, Nailhead spar, Dogtooth spar, Beef) *Calcium carbonate* ($CaCO_3$)   It is the main component of limestone, marble and chalk. It is also commonly found as kettle fur and boiler scale in hard water districts and is the mineral of which most fossil shells are made. Dissolved calcite is precipitated by the evaporation of dripping water in limestone caves as stalagmites and stalactites.

Crystals are common and there are several forms: nailhead spar, dogtooth spar and rhombohedral crystals which, when clear, are called Iceland spar. Scalenohedral crystals occur, and also fibrous calcite, which is sometimes known by the quarryman's term, 'beef'.

Calcite is usually translucent with a vitreous lustre, but may be transparent or opaque. It is colourless when pure, but can be almost any colour, including black. The specific gravity is 2.6–2.8, which is similar to dolomite but much lighter than siderite. Calcite is softer than either with a hardness of 3 on most crystal faces, but less on the base of the crystal, which has a hardness of 2 and can be scratched by a fingernail. This relative softness distinguishes calcite from quartz, which is of similar appearance. Another distinguishing feature is the rhombohedral cleavage, which can be seen as cracks in transparent calcite and as rhombohedral steps on broken specimens. Powdered calcite consists of minute cleavage rhombohedra which can be seen if the powder is examined under a magnifying lens. Calcite effervesces readily with dilute acid whereas other carbonates react slowly and may have to be warmed.

The clear variety of calcite known as Iceland spar exhibits the property of double refraction possessed to a lesser degree by many crystals. The mineral splits light into two rays

Rhombohedral crystals of dolomite from Eugui, Navarra, Spain

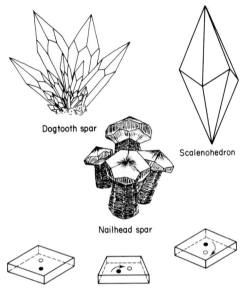

Dogtooth spar

Scalenohedron

Nailhead spar

Iceland spar showing double refraction

CALCITE

which produce a double image. A dot on a piece of paper appears as two dots if a crystal of Iceland spar is placed over it and one dot, the 'ghost image', moves around the other as the crystal is rotated on the paper.

In addition to its occurrence as a rock-forming mineral, calcite is found as a common gangue mineral in low temperature hydrothermal veins. The best crystals are formed in cavities, and Iceland spar was first found not in veins but in lava cavities in Iceland. It is used to make lenses for special optical work.

Dolomite (Pearl spar) *Magnesium and calcium carbonate* $(CaMg[CO_3]_2)$ Unlike calcite and siderite, it does not form scalenohedra. The crystals are rhombohedral, usually with curved faces, and combine to form saddle shaped growths.

Dolomite can be white but is more often grey, pink or honey coloured. The crystals are translucent and have a pearly lustre, rhombohedral cleavage and white streak. The specific gravity of 2.8 increases as dolomite grades into siderite. The hardness is $3\frac{1}{2}$–4 and this, with the pearly lustre and curved crystals, helps to distinguish dolomite from calcite. Unlike calcite, dolomite effervesces very slowly with dilute acid.

Dolomite is a major constituent of dolomitic limestones and also occurs as a gangue mineral in veins with sphalerite or galena. It is usually the first mineral to be deposited, so it lies on the outside of the vein, against the wall rock.

Dolomite is used for furnace linings, special cements and as a flux in blast furnaces. It is also a source of magnesium metal and magnesia for medical uses.

Gypsum (Selenite, Satinspar, Alabaster) *Hydrous calcium sulphate* $(CaSO_4 \cdot 2H_2O)$ Found in three forms: first, selenite is the name for the crystals, which are generally tabular and often form swallowtail twins. Prismatic crystals also occur, and these are often curved or bent. Crystals of selenite have a platy cleavage, which produces thin flexible sheets. The second form is fibrous; it is found when gypsum occurs in veins and it is known as satinspar or 'beef'. In its third form, found in evaporite deposits, gypsum is granular, and alabaster is the name for the fine-grained granular form.

Gypsum has a hardness of 2 on Mohs' scale so it is not only sectile and easy to carve but can be scratched with a fingernail, which distinguishes it from harder calcite and anhydrite. It is also lighter in weight with a specific gravity of 2.3. It is a colourless mineral but may be stained a variety of colours. Selenite is transparent with a vitreous or pearly lustre. Other varieties are translucent and alabaster has a pearly and satinspar a silky lustre.

Above: yellow cubes of fluorite with galena, from Weardale, Co. Durham, UK

Above: vase of Blue John, a variety of fluorite from Derbyshire, UK

Left: interpenetrating purple cubes of fluorite from Alston Moor, Cumbria, UK

Gypsum is a common mineral which forms thick beds in evaporite deposits, where it is often associated with halite. Selenite crystals are found in blue clays such as the London and Oxford clays, where they were produced by the reaction between shells and sulphuric acid released by the decay of pyrite. In many places in the Sahara, gypsum crystals formed by the evaporation of salt lakes are found buried in the sand. The crystals enclose grains of sand as they grow and form flower-like aggregates known as desert roses.

When gypsum is heated it loses some of its water of crystallization and becomes a powder. This reverts to gypsum when water is added, and subsequently sets hard. This powder is known as plaster of Paris because it was first made there from gypsum quarried at Montmartre. Plaster of Paris is used today for making plaster casts for broken bones, and the plaster that is applied to walls and ceilings. Gypsum is used in paint and as a fertilizer, and a small proportion of the gypsum produced is used for 'burtonizing', or artificially hardening, water for brewing beer.

Fluorite (Fluorspar, Blue John, Derbyshire spar) *Calcium fluoride* (CaF_2) It forms distinctive interpenetrating cubes, which may be colour banded and show octahedral cleavage. Octahedra and single cubes of fluorite also occur in veins but is usually granular. The mineral is transparent and colourless when pure, but more often it is yellow, green, blue or purple, with a vitreous lustre. It has a white streak and is the standard mineral for a hardness of 4 on Mohs' scale. It gave its name to the phenomenon of fluorescence because some crystals of fluorite glow in ultraviolet light. The mineral can be recognized by its form, cleavage and hardness, which is greater than that of calcite, but less than that of quartz.

Fluorite is a hydrothermal mineral usually found as a gangue in veins with argentite, galena, sphalerite, quartz and barytes. It also occurs in cavities in limestone and dolomite, and as a cement in some sandstones.

The ancient Greeks and Romans carved fluorite into

murrhine vases, and the variety found in Derbyshire known as Blue John has been used more recently for similar decorative purposes. Although in the past it has been considered a gangue mineral, now it is mined in many parts of the world for a variety of industrial purposes. It is used to make hydrofluoric acid, enamels and opalescent glass. It is a constituent of some toothpastes and is used to produce refrigerants and fluorocarbon resin coatings for lining non-stick pans. Inferior grades of fluorite are used as a flux in steelmaking. The specific gravity of fluorite is 3.1–3.2.

Sulphur (Brimstone) (S) Native sulphur is a bright yellow substance, either crystalline or amorphous. It has been known since biblical times as brimstone, which simply means burning stone. It can be ignited by a match flame and melts to a dark yellow liquid and burns with a blue flame, producing choking fumes of sulphur dioxide.

Impure earthy sulphur may be brown, amber, red or green. The crystals have a resinous lustre and are brittle with conchoidal fracture. They are very light with a specific gravity of 2 and a hardness of 1.5 to 2.5. They must be handled as little as possible because they expand and crack in the warmth of a hand. Friction gives sulphur crystals a negative electric charge. The mineral can be recognized by its colour, light weight, softness and above all by its fumes when burnt.

Sulphur is deposited where there is volcanic activity, and this may explain the association of brimstone with the fires of hell. In Japan, Italy and Chile sulphur is mined from extinct volcanoes. It forms around fumaroles as a sublimation from volcanic gases, for example in the Valley of Ten Thousand Smokes in Alaska, and it is deposited from hot springs and crater lakes. Most of the world's sulphur today comes from altered limestone or gypsum in Poland and Sicily and the Gulf of Mexico.

Sulphur is used to make gunpowder, safety matches, ointments, dyes, fungicides, fertilizer, as a bleach for paper and for vulcanizing rubber to make it harder and less sticky.

Translucent crystals of sulphur from Agrigento, Sicily, showing resinous lustre

Quartz (Tiger's eye, Amethyst, Rock crystal, Citrine, Cairngorm, Morion etc) *Silica or silicon dioxide* (SiO_2) The commonest mineral in the earth's crust and is found in all but the basic and ultrabasic rocks. Quartzites and sandstones consist almost entirely of quartz. Despite the abundance of the mineral, some varieties are valued as semi-precious stones.

Vein quartz is massive, white and translucent or opaque; and transparent crystals are frequently found in cavities known as druses. They also occur in hollow globular forms called geodes. The crystals are prismatic and six-sided, terminating in a point and the faces may have horizontal striations. Japan twins sometimes occur but they are not common. Good crystals are transparent with a vitreous lustre and may be almost any colour. Amethyst is purple

Quartz:
crystals and a
group of cut
stones
including
tiger's eye,
citrine and
amethyst

quartz, citrine is yellow, cairngorm or smoky quartz is brown, morion black. Tiger's eye is fibrous quartz which has replaced crocidolite asbestos.

Quartz has a hardness of 7 on Mohs' scale: it scratches glass but cannot be scratched by a knife. It is harder than most colourless minerals and has a specific gravity of 2.6, thus being lighter than other semi-precious stones. This, together with its less brilliant lustre, distinguishes quartz from diamond.

Quartz is the most common vein mineral and the chief constituent of sandstone, quartzite and beach and desert sand. It is an essential mineral in granite and is often found in other igneous rocks. It is one of the main minerals in schists and gneisses. Some of the best specimens come from cavities known as crystal caves in the schists of the Swiss Alps. The largest crystals, some of which have a circumference of several metres, are found in Madagascar.

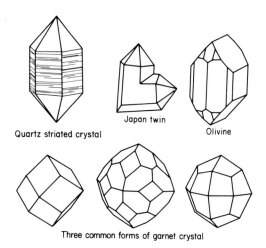

Quartz striated crystal

Japan twin

Olivine

Three common forms of garnet crystal

Perfect quartz crystals are used as oscillators in radios and electronic watches. A great deal of quartz is melted and used in porcelain, pottery and glass making. Sand is a useful abrasive in the form of sandpaper, and rock crystal has been used for many years in the making of lenses for telescopes, microscopes and other optical instruments.

Chalcedony (Jasper, Chrysoprase, Bloodstone, Agate, Onyx, Flint) *Microcrystalline quartz* (SiO_2) Most usually forms at low temperatures and is translucent to opaque with a dull or waxy lustre. This distinguishes it from crystalline quartz, though it has the same conchoidal fracture and is similar in hardness and specific gravity. It often lines cavities and veins, and can be botryoidal or stalactitic. Jasper is a red, yellow or brown variety coloured by iron oxides, chrysoprase is apple green and bloodstone green with red spots. Agate has irregular, sometimes circular bands of colour and often replaces fossil wood. Onyx is similar but with straight bands of alternate light and dark material. Moss agate contains moss-like aggregates of pyrolusite. The best known type of chalcedony is flint, which is usually grey or black and often contains tiny quartz crystals in cavities. Chalcedony is slightly porous and is often artificially dyed for ornamental use.

Opal *Amorphous silica* (SiO_2+nH_2O) A solidified jelly so it has no crystal structure and contains up to 13 per cent water. It may be white or colourless, grey, brown or red. The iridescent colours for which opal is prized are due to the play of light on hairline cracks within the mineral. Opal is absorbent and water taken in through the cracks enhances the iridescence while grease dulls it.

Opal is usually translucent, has a waxy lustre and is slightly lighter and softer than chalcedony, which it otherwise resembles. It is deposited from solution and is often found in the joints and cavities of igneous rocks, replacing fossils in tuffs, and builds up around geysers and hot springs like those of Rotorua in New Zealand. The best gem opals are found in cracks in an Australian sandstone.

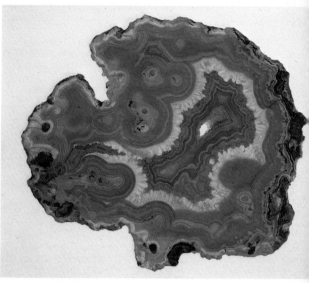

Agate: a banded variety of quartz, from Laguna, Chihuahua, Mexico

The name comes from *upala*, a Sanskrit word simply meaning a stone. Hardness $5\frac{1}{2}$–$6\frac{1}{2}$, specific gravity 1.9–2.3.

Orthoclase (Potash felspar, Moonstone) *Potassium aluminium silicate* ($K[AlSi_3]O_8$) A groups of light coloured silicates which together make up an estimated 60 per cent of the earth's crust. Orthoclase is the typical felspar of acid igneous rocks and in arkose sandstones derived from them. Most of the large, white or pink crystals in granites are orthoclase. The crystals occur as short prisms which are often twinned; they have two cleavages at right angles, which causes the mineral to break into rectangular fragments. Felspar twinning often shows if a piece of granite is turned so that the sun catches the two halves of a crystal, which reflect the light at different angles. Carlsbad twins are

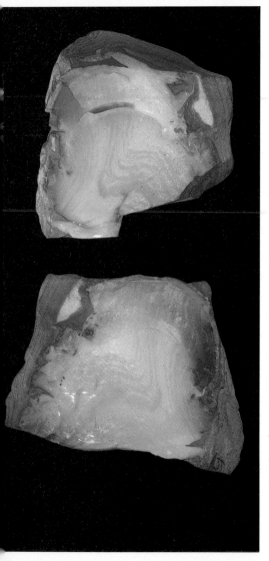

Opal from Queensland, Australia, showing the play of colours

the most common, but baveno and manebach twins also occur.

Orthoclase is usually white or flesh pink, and translucent to opaque with a vitreous lustre, or in some cases pearly lustre on cleavage faces. It has a hardness of 6 and can just be scratched by a knife, unlike quartz. It can also be distinguished from quartz by its duller lustre, as well as by its two cleavage planes at right angles. Orthoclase has a specific gravity of 2.5, very close to that of quartz, and for this reason the two are often deposited together in arkose.

Orthoclase is difficult to distinguish from plagioclase without the aid of a microscope, but it lacks the polysynthetic twinning, and plagioclase is seldom pink.

Gneisses often contain recrystallized orthoclase, and it is one of the principal minerals in pegmatite. Crystals several feet long have been found in pegmatites, and in Canada,

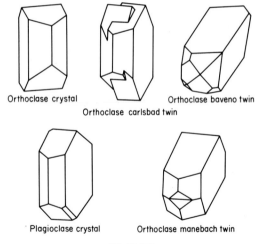

Orthoclase crystal

Orthoclase baveno twin

Orthoclase carlsbad twin

Plagioclase crystal

Orthoclase manebach twin

FELSPARS

Norway, Sweden and the USA these are mined for use in porcelain, enamel, opalescent glass and fertilizers. A milky variety of orthoclase is called moonstone.

Plagioclase (Soda-lime felspar, Albite, Oligoclase, Andesine, Labradorite, Bytownite, Anorthite) *Sodium and calcium aluminium silicates* ($Na[AlSi_3O_8]$ – Albite), ($Ca[Al_2Si_2O_8]$ – Anorthite)   Group of minerals ranging in composition from sodium aluminium silicate to calcium aluminium silicate. Plagioclase crystals are short prisms usually showing polysynthetic twinning, but carlsbad manebach and baveno twins are sometimes found. Granular masses can be recognized by their rectangular cleavage and vitreous lustre, sometimes pearly on cleavage faces. Plagioclase is usually white or colourless but the variety labradorite shows a play of colours, usually dark blue and green. Like orthoclase, plagioclase has a hardness of 6 and specific gravity of 2.6, but plagioclase can sometimes be distinguished by its polysynthetic twinning. Labradorite is mined for ornamental use not only in Labrador but near Kiev in the Ukraine, Ojamo in Finland, and in New York State. Plagioclase is the essential felspar in basic igneous rocks such as basalt, and is found in some schists and gneisses.

Muscovite (White mica, Muscovy glass) *Potassium aluminium silicate* ($KAl_2[OH,F]_2AlSi_3O_{10}$)   A colourless and silvery or pale grey transparent mineral with a pearly lustre, found as flakes in many rocks. It is common in pegmatites, sometimes forming tabular six-sided crystals, which may be two or three metres across. These can be split into very thin cleavage plates which are flexible and elastic and may show a six pointed star when held before a light. The elastic cleavage plates distinguish muscovite from chlorite, and the colour distinguishes it from biotite.

Muscovite is a major constituent of metamorphic rocks and is particularly noticeable in mica schists and phyllites. It also occurs in siltstones and some sandstones, and in acid igneous rocks. Its hardness is 2–3, specific gravity 2.8.

Very large crystals are found in the Ural Mountains,

Twinned crystal of orthoclase felspar from Brevik, Norway

Oligoclase, a variety of plagioclase felspar, from Drangedal, Norway

Biotite crystal from Monti Albani, Italy

Ontario, Canada and in New Hampshire and South Dakota, USA. The name is derived from Muscovy, an old name for Russia, one of the first countries to utilize it into a kind of window glass. Muscovite is still used for making windows, but only in stove and furnace doors where its great resistance to heat gives it an advantage over glass. It is also an electrical insulator, and it is ground up to make lubricants, artificial stone and Christmas frost.

Biotite (Dark mica) *Potassium magnesium iron aluminium silicate* ($K[Mg,Fe]_3AlSi_3O_{10}[OH,F]_2$) Common in rocks as flakes and six-sided crystals with perfect cleavage. Large crystals look like books, and it is easy to peel off thin 'pages' which are flexible and elastic. If a cleavage flake is struck with a blunt point it produces a percussion figure like a six rayed star. Dark brown is the usual colour but biotite may be black or very dark green; when it occurs in mass it is translucent with a vitreous lustre. Cleavage flakes may be transparent and often have a pearly or coppery metallic sheen.

The hardness of biotite is $2\frac{1}{2}$–3 and the specific gravity ranges from 2.8 to 3.4, depending on the amount of iron present. It can be distinguished from muscovite by its colour, and from other dark silicates by its cleavage.

Biotite is often found with muscovite in granites, schists and gneisses. Very large mica books are found in some pegmatites.

Biotite is used in electrical apparatus and is ground up for dusting rubber goods and asphalt tiles to prevent them from sticking together.

Chlorite *Magnesium iron aluminium silicates* ($(Fe,Mg,Al)_6[(OH)_2 + (Si,Al)_4O_{10}]$) Complex silicates which are stable at low temperatures. They are similar to the micas and are often formed by the alteration of biotite and other mafic minerals.

Chlorite is a scaly, sometimes hexagonal mineral, with platy cleavage and flexible but not elastic flakes. Typical chlorite is green but it can be white, yellow, brown or nearly black. It may be earthy, or translucent with a vitreous or pearly lustre. It varies in hardness from 2–3 and has a greasy feel. The specific gravity increases with the iron content from 2.6 to 3.3. Chlorite can be recognized by its colour and cleavage and the hardness which is greater than that of talc.

Chlorite is formed in low grade metamorphic rocks, especially green schists. It is a common alteration product of biotite, augite and hornblende and can often be seen in weathered igneous rocks. It can be found as green streaks, on a fault where rocks have slipped past one another, and fills vesicles in some lavas. Chamosite, an iron-rich chlorite, is important in some sedimentary iron ores.

Glauconite *A complex iron and potassium silicate* $(CaNa_2[SO_4]_2)$ It is a member of the mica family, usually found as rounded grains in sedimentary rocks or coatings on pebbles. The name is derived from the Greek *glaukos*, which means blue-green. Glauconite is dark green, opaque and dull, and may be so abundant that it colours the rock green, forming a variety of sandstone known as greensand. The hardness of glauconite on Mohs' scale is $2\frac{1}{2}$–3 and the specific gravity between 2.7 and 2.8.

Amphiboles *Iron magnesium calcium sodium silicates* $(Ca_2[MgFe]_5[OH]_2$ – Actinolite) A complex silicate family rich in iron and magnesium. They are common in igneous and metamorphic rocks and similar in appearance to the pyroxenes. Amphiboles often form bladed or fibrous aggregates, unlike pyroxenes, which tend to form stumpy crystals. The minerals are most easily distinguished by the patterns produced by the intersection of their two cleavage planes. Amphibole cleavage planes intersect at an angle of $124°$, giving a diamond pattern, whereas the cleavage planes of pyroxenes intersect almost at right angles.

Hornblende (Common amphibole) $([Ca,Na,K]_{2-3}[Mg,Fe,Al]_5[(OH,F)_2+(Si,Al)_2Si_6O_{22}])$ Colour varies from green to black and it forms translucent prismatic crystals, transparent on broken edges. The lustre is vitreous. Hardness is 5–6 and

Above: augite and hornblende. Left, two crystals of augite.
Right, two crystals of hornblende

specific gravity is 2.9–3.4. Black hornblende might be confused with tourmaline but the cleavage is distinctive.

Diorite and andesite usually contain hornblende and it is found in some granites and syenites. Hornblende schists and gneisses occur in regionally metamorphosed areas. Rocks which consist almost entirely of hornblende are known as amphibolites.

Nephrite (Jade) Nephrite is made up of interlocking fibres of two amphiboles. It is one of the varieties of jade and is highly prized as an ornamental stone, especially by the Chinese. Although amphiboles only have a hardness of about 5–6, nephrite is very tough and has been used from Neolithic times to the present day for making stone axe-heads.

Nephrite has been mined in China for thousands of years and in New Zealand it was used by the Maoris for tools and tiki carvings.

A polished slab of nephrite jade

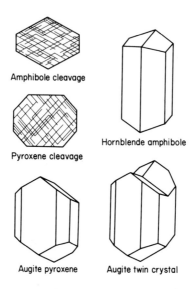

Amphibole cleavage

Pyroxene cleavage

Hornblende amphibole

Augite pyroxene

Augite twin crystal

Asbestos　Three varieties of amphibole are used as asbestos. They are all heat resistant and occur in fibrous form. The minerals of which asbestos is the fibrous form have normal amphibole hardness but appear soft because the fibres easily separate when the mineral is scratched.

Some varieties of asbestos are brittle, and are suitable only for wallboard and insulating paints and cement. The stronger fibres can be spun into cloth for safety curtains, brake linings and fireproof protective clothing. They are mostly shades of green or brown but crocidolite which is mined in South Africa and Western Australia is blue. It may be partly or completely replaced by quartz to form tiger's eye, sometimes keeping the blue colour, sometimes altering to golden yellow.

Pyroxenes *Calcium magnesium iron aluminium silicates* ($Mg[SiO_3]_2$ – Enstatite) An important family of complex rock-forming minerals. They are very similar in appearance to amphiboles but usually form short prismatic crystals which are square or octagonal in cross section and have two sets of cleavages almost at right angles to one another. Enstatite hardness $5\frac{1}{2}$, specific gravity 3.15–3.176.

Augite ($[Ca,Mg,Fe_2,Ti,Al]_2(Si,Al)_2O_6]$) The commonest pyroxene, translucent and black or greenish black with a vitreous to resinous lustre. It has a hardness of 5–6 and specific gravity of 3.2–3.5. Basalt, gabbro and peridotite usually contain abundant augite and so do some andesites. The tuffs deposited around some volcanoes consist almost entirely of augite crystals, and crystals up to an inch long can be picked out of weathered lavas in the crater of Vesuvius.

Jadeite (Jade) *A sodium aluminium silicate* ($NaAl[Si_2O_6]$) A pyroxene with minutely fibrous structure which gives it an almost silky lustre and an exceptional resistance to breaking. It varies in colour from emerald green, blue-green, apple green to white spotted with green. It is the mineral known as jade which has been used for thousands of years for carving jewellery and ornaments, particularly by the Chinese. It was also used for making tools before metals were discovered. Hardness 6–7, specific gravity 3.2–3.4.

Olivine (Peridot, Chrysolite) *Magnesium iron silicate* ($[Mg,Fe]_2SiO_4$) Derives its name from usual olive green colour, but there are also golden yellow varieties, and these have been known by the older name of chrysolite. This name is seldom used now because it is easily confused with chrysotile, a kind of asbestos. Olivine occurs in prismatic eight sided crystals and granular masses which form the rock dunite.

The crystals are transparent and have a vitreous lustre and conchoidal fracture but are often altered to serpentine along the cracks, imparting a cloudy appearance. The hardness varies from $6\frac{1}{2}$–7 and the specific gravity from 3.3–4.2

Olivine: a group showing dunite rock, a crystal and several cut and polished stones

Garnet: a group of crystals and cut stones showing the variety of colours

depending on the proportion of magnesium to iron in the mineral. Olivine reacts with silica in crystallizing magma to form pyroxene so olivine and quartz are seldom found in the same rock.

Olivine occurs in basalts such as those of Hawaii, in ultrabasic peridotite and dunite and in stony meteorites. It is common in basalts on the moon, and is thought to be the most abundant mineral in the earth's mantle, the layer below the crust. Olivine is a high temperature mineral and quickly alters to serpentine once it reaches the earth's surface so gem quality crystals which are known as peridots are very rare. The tiny island of St John in the Red Sea produces good crystals and was probably the source of ancient Egyptian gems. Burma and Minas Gerais in Brazil also yield gem quality peridots.

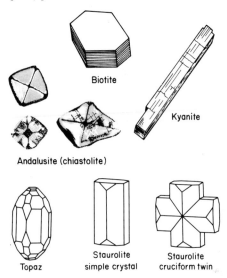

Biotite

Kyanite

Andalusite (chiastolite)

Topaz

Staurolite simple crystal

Staurolite cruciform twin

Garnets (Pyrope, Almandine, Spessartite, Uvarovite, Grossularite, Andradite) *A complex silicate group* ($Mg_3Al_2[SiO_4]_3$ – Pyrope) Common in granular aggregate, garnets often occur as rhombdodecahedral or trapezohedral crystals, or in combinations of the two forms.

Garnet has a hardness of $7-7\frac{1}{2}$, a specific gravity of 3.6 to 4.3. It can be transparent or opaque with a vitreous or resinous lustre and the most common colour is reddish brown. Other colours are pink, violet, yellow, green and occasionally black but the best known type of garnet is the red semi-precious stone pyrope, one of several red gems which used to be called carbuncles.

Garnets develop at high temperatures in a variety of rocks, especially schists and gneisses and contact metamorphic rocks such as skarn, which forms where limestone is intruded by magma. Garnets are resistant to weathering and are found in placer deposits, especially where these are derived from areas of regional metamorphism, as in the Highlands of Scotland.

Pyrope is particularly suitable for jewel bearings in clocks and scientific instruments; much of the gem quality pyrope comes from the Slovakian Republic. Crushed garnet is also used industrially as an abrasive powder, or glued to polishing cloths and papers and used for finishing wood and leather.

Andalusite (Chiastolite) *Aluminium silicate* (Al_2SiO_5) Named after the Spanish province of Andalusia, it is the high temperature form of aluminium silicate and is usually seen as spots in contact metamorphosed slates and hornfelses near an igneous intrusion. The crystals of andalusite are prismatic with a square cross section, and the variety known as chiastolite contains tiny specks of carbon, which form a dark cross.

The mineral is usually pink, red or grey, and varies from transparent to nearly opaque with a vitreous lustre. Its specific gravity is 3.1–3.2 and its hardness is $7\frac{1}{2}$. Andalusite alters to silvery mica which may coat the crystals and make them seem softer.

Andalusite can be distinguished by its square prismatic

Andalusite (chiastolite) from Bimbowrie, South Australia showing the cross shapes formed by minute inclusions in the crystal

Kyanite: bladed crystals from Chesterfield, Mass., USA

form, hardness and the fact that it is found mainly in metamorphic rocks, especially contact metamorphosed shales. There is an important deposit at White Mountains, California. The andalusite from here is used for making porcelain with a high heat resistance, much of which is used in spark plugs. At Minas Gerais in Brazil transparent green waterworn crystals are found and cut as gems. Large chiastolite crystals are found in Brittany and the Pyrenees and at Santiago de Compostella in northern Spain they have been polished and sold to pilgrims as 'stones of the Cross' since mediaeval times.

Kyanite (Disthene) *Aluminium silicate* (Al_2SiO_5) An attractive blue mineral commonly occurring as bladed crystals and radiating aggregates in high grade metamorphic rocks such as schists and gneisses. It is the variety of aluminium silicate that remains stable under stress. Though usually blue, kyanite is sometimes white, grey or green. The colour may be patchy, and is usually darker toward the centre of the crystal. The crystal is transparent to translucent and has a vitreous lustre. Kyanite has a specific gravity of 3.5–3.7 and a hardness of 4–5 along crystals but 6–7 across them. A steel knife will therefore scratch a crystal in one direction but not the other. The name disthene is Greek for double strength and refers to this difference in hardness.

Kyanite is distinguished by its colour, bladed habit and variable hardness and by its occurrence with staurolite and garnet in rocks metamorphosed under stress.

Waterworn crystals from Brazil are used as gemstones but ordinary kyanite is used in the manufacture of high grade porcelain for heat resistant bricks and spark plugs.

Sillimanite (Fibrolite) *Aluminium silicate* (Al_2SiO_5) Forms fibrous and acicular aggregates, usually white but also grey, brown, green or light blue. Crystals large enough to identify are rare, but when found they prove to be transparent to translucent, with a vitreous lustre. The hardness is 6–7 though fibres seem softer, and the specific gravity is 3.2. The hardness distinguishes sillimanite from asbestos. It is often altered to muscovite.

Sillimanite is found in rocks metamorphosed at high temperatures under moderate stress, in high grade regionally metamorphosed rocks and in the inner zone of hornfelses. In Sri Lanka it is found in the unusual form of gem quality waterworn blue pebbles. Similar pebbles from Brazil are cut to resemble cat's eyes.

Staurolite *Iron aluminium silicate* $(Al_4FeOOH[SiO_4]_2$ It occurs as crystals but is more often twinned in the form of a cross, hence the name from the Greek *stauros*, a cross. The colour is golden- or reddish-brown to black, varying from translucent to opaque with a dull, roughened surface but with a vitreous to resinous lustre inside. The streak is colourless or greyish, the hardness $7-7\frac{1}{2}$, and the specific gravity 3.7. Staurolite is distinguished by its colour and twinning and its occurrence in regionally metamorphosed gneisses and mica schists often with garnet, kyanite and sillimanite. In Virginia the crystals are called fairy crosses and worn as good luck charms.

Topaz *Aluminium fluorine silicate* $(Al_2F_2SiO_4)$ One of the few gem minerals which, under suitable conditions, grow into enormous crystals. The crystals are prismatic, often with vertical striations on the faces, and transparent with a vitreous lustre. Shades of yellow are the most common, but colourless and sometimes pale green, blue or pink crystals are found.

Topaz has a hardness of 8 and is distinguished by its hardness from minerals like quartz and corundum, which occur in similar colour varieties. It has a fairly high specific gravity of 3.6–3.7 and so may be found in placer deposits.

Topaz originates in cavities in granite and rhyolite, in pegmatites and in high temperature mineral veins with cassiterite and tourmaline. Topaz occurs in the Mourne Mountains granite, and blue waterworn crystals are found in the Cairngorms. The largest known deposits are at Minas Gerais in Brazil where huge boulders and crystals 30 cm (12 in) or more across have been found.

Heating changes the colour of some topazes, and in this way collectors or jewellers are able to alter the brown gems to the rarer and therefore more valuable pink colour.

Apatite *Calcium phosphate with fluorine and chlorine* (Ca[F,Cl][PO$_4$]$_3$ It forms prismatic crystals which are easily confused with beryl. Shades of green are most common and crystals are transparent to opaque, with a resinous or vitreous lustre. The hardness is 5 so apatite can just be scratched by a knife, unlike beryl or green tourmaline. Specific gravity is 3.16–3.22.

Apatite is common in pegmatites, metamorphosed limestones and high temperature hydrothermal veins. It is the most abundant phosphorus bearing mineral in the earth's crust and as phosphorus is necessary for plant growth it is an important fertilizer. Apatite is the main constituent of teeth and bones, and where fossil bones accumulate in sufficient quantity they form phosphate rock. This consists largely of amorphous apatite which is grey, white, yellow or brown.

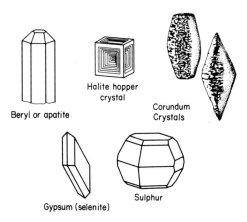

Beryl or apatite

Halite hopper
crystal

Corundum
Crystals

Gypsum (selenite)

Sulphur

On oceanic islands phosphate rock, which is a mixture of calcite and apatite, is formed by the reaction between bird droppings and limestone. Both types of phosphate rock are mined for use as fertilizer, and in Kazakhstan apatite is obtained from syenite for the same purpose.

Apatite is also used as a gem. The yellow–green variety known as asparagus stone is the most popular variety and is found at Jumilla in Spain and at Durango, Mexico.

Beryl (Emerald, Aquamarine, Heliodor, Morganite) *Beryllium aluminium silicate* ($Al_2Be_3[Si_6O_{18}]$) Beryl forms hexagonal prismatic crystals, but it can also occur in granular masses. The most common colour is green, and emeralds are gem quality green crystals of beryl. Blue–green aquamarine, yellow heliodor and pink morganite are also varieties of beryl.

Beryl has a vitreous to resinous lustre and is transparent to translucent; the coarser varieties are opaque. The streak is white but obtained with difficulty as beryl has a hardness of $7\frac{1}{2}$–8. Hardness distinguishes beryl from apatite, and its specific gravity of 2.7 is much less than that of corundum.

Beryl is most often found in pegmatites but also occurs in granites and the metamorphosed rocks around them. Large crystals are found in druses in the Mourne Mountains granite, and in the Urals beryl crystals are found in pegmatite and in the surrounding mica schists. Colombia produces the best emeralds; Madagascar yields large morganite crystals; and at Minas Gerais in Brazil aquamarines weighing several hundred kg have been taken from stream beds.

Clear crystals are used as gemstones but beryl is also a source of beryllium, used in special alloys. Beryl suitable for this purpose is a by product of the production of felspar and mica from pegmatites.

Tourmaline (Schorl) *A complex ferromagnesian silicate containing boron* ($Na[Mg,Fe,Li,Al,Mn]_3Al_6[BO_3]_3O_{18}[OH,F]_4$) Tourmaline was known for centuries by the name of schorl. Coloured crystals were imported from Sri Lanka at

Transparent prismatic crystal of topaz from Urul'ga river, Nerchinsk, Chitinskaya, CIS

Emerald (a variety of beryl): hexagonal crystal in a matrix of calcite, from Colombia

the beginning of the eighteenth century and given the Sinhalese name of *turmali* or *toramalli*. These imported crystals were mostly red or pink, but green, blue, brown and yellow crystals also occur. The coloured varieties of tourmaline are transparent and were at first considered to be a different mineral from schorl, which is nearly opaque.

All varieties, coloured and black, have a vitreous lustre and pale streak. Tourmaline has a hardness of $7-7\frac{1}{2}$ and a specific gravity of $3-3.3$ which makes it occur commonly in placer deposits. The crystals are triangular prisms, longitudinally striated, and often occur in columnar or acicular radiating aggregates. There is often one colour at the centre of a crystal and another colour outside, or the two ends of the crystal may be different colours. The Isle of Elba is famous for pink crystals tipped with black which are known as Moors' Heads. Transparent crystals are also dichroic – the depth of colour varies as the crystal is turned in the light.

Another peculiarity of tourmaline is that a crystal when heated acquires an electric charge and will attract small objects such as a hair or piece of tissue paper. Rubbing the crystal imparts a similar charge.

Tourmaline is found in granites and gneisses, and is especially common in pegmatites. It is often found in hydrothermal veins with cassiterite and topaz. Tourmaline also occurs in metamorphosed limestones with corundum.

The coloured varieties of tourmaline are used as gems. Pala in California and Minas Gerais in Brazil are famous for these, and in Madagascar large crystals with interesting colour zones are found. Tourmaline is used in electrical apparatus and in the construction of pressure gauges.

Talc (Soapstone, Steatite, Potstone) *Hydrous magnesium silicate* $(Mg_3Si_4O_{10}[OH]_2)$ Used in most bathrooms but in nature this is a soft scaly mineral with a greasy or soapy feel. Mixed with chlorite it forms a soft rock variously known as soapstone, potstone or steatite.

Pure talc is white but it is often coloured grey or shades of pale green by traces of chlorite. Talc has a pearly or greasy lustre and a soapy feel. It is the standard mineral of hardness 1 on Mohs' scale and is very sectile. No other light-coloured mineral is as soft. The streak is white and talc is used as tailor's chalk for marking cloth. The specific gravity is 2.7 for pure talc.

Talc is usually a secondary mineral. It is formed by the alteration of magnesium-rich rocks such as peridotite and gabbro. Talc is also found in some schists and in metamorphosed dolomite.

The USA is predominant in the world's production of talc, with deposits in New York State (carbonate rocks), in Vermont and Virginia. Europe's largest deposits are in Italy and Austria, where an apple green talc occurs.

Steatite has been used for carvings for thousands of years because of its softness and the fact that it hardens a little on heating or exposure to air. In some non-technical societies steatite has been used for pots and griddles because of its resistance to fire. It is also used as French chalk for polishing, in soap, paints, baby- and face-powder, for dusting rubber and as a filler in plastics. It is used to remove grease from cloth and leather, and in special ceramic insulators.

Serpentine (Chrysotile asbestos) *A complex magnesium silicate* ($Mg_6[OH]_8Si_4O_{10}$)   A secondary mineral formed by the alteration of magnesium-rich silicates, especially olivine and pyroxene. Chrysotile, a fibrous variety of serpentine, is the most valued type of asbestos because the fibres are more flexible than those of amphibole asbestos. Chrysotile has a silky lustre and the fibres can be separated by rubbing between the fingers.

Massive serpentine occurs in shades of green, sometimes streaked and spotted with red and brown. It is translucent to opaque with a greasy lustre. Serpentine is sectile and easy to carve with a hardness varying from 3–4. The hardness distinguishes it from chlorite, which is softer, and jade, which is harder. The specific gravity is 2.5–2.6.

Serpentine is produced when peridotite is altered by the addition of water; a process which often also produces talc, veins of which are often found in serpentine. A rock

composed almost entirely of serpentine is called serpentinite, and is often brecciated by the expansion which takes place as the original minerals alter to serpentine. The name serpentine refers to the streaked and spotted appearance, which is supposed to resemble snakeskin.

Serpentine occurs at the Lizard in Cornwall, Turin in Italy and Thetford in Canada, where the world's largest serpentine asbestos deposits are situated.

Asbestos is used to make fireproof clothing. Chrysotile is so fine that a kilogram of it can be spun into about 15,000 m of thread. Its many other uses include fireproof wallboards and roofing asbestos, brake linings and heat resistant paint.

Recently asbestos dust has been recognized as a health hazard. It causes a disease called asbestosis if it is inhaled over a period of many years, and it can also cause cancer. Factories

Left: variegated tourmaline crystal with quartz, from USA

Right: vein of chrysotile asbestos in serpentine, from Quebec, Canada

making asbestos products have to take special precautions, and alternative minerals are being used wherever possible.

Corundum (Ruby, Sapphire) *Aluminium oxide* (Al_2O_3) By far the best-known varieties are ruby and sapphire. The mineral is colourless when pure and may also be grey, green, yellow or violet. It can be granular or form barrel or spindle shaped crystals which when cut are transparent and have an adamantine lustre. Naturally occurring specimens are usually dull and greasy looking with a hardness of 9.

Corundum has a specific gravity of 3.9–4.1, enabling the crystals to be separated easily from sediments by panning. This and the fact that it is the hardest natural substance apart from diamond makes corundum easy to identify.

Most of the corundum produced today comes from

placer deposits derived from igneous rocks and contact metamorphosed limestones. The best and most ancient sources of ruby and sapphire are Burma, Thailand, Kashmir and Sri Lanka. The finest rubies, of pigeon's blood red, come from Mogok in Burma, whilst Thailand and Cambodia produce deep cornflower blue sapphires.

Flawless crystals have been used for thousands of years as gemstones, and natural crystals were probably used to carve stone monuments when the only metal tools available were made of copper or bronze. Less than perfect gems are used as bearings in watches, and granular corundum is important as an abrasive. Emery is a natural mixture of corundum, magnetite and haematite and is used as an abrasive.

Halite (Common salt or Rock salt) *Sodium chloride* (NaCl)
Look at some table salt under a lens and you will see the cubic crystal form of halite. Crystals grown by slowly evaporating a strong salt solution often have concave hopper-shaped faces, but rock salt is massive and granular and superficially resembles marble. It is colourless or white but may contain impurities which stain it red, grey, brown, yellow or blue.

Crystals are transparent and have a vitreous lustre, perfect cubic cleavage, and a hardness of 2. Halite is a very light mineral with a specific gravity of 2.1–2.2. It is soluble in cold water and can be recognized by its salty taste. This helps to distinguish halite from potassium chloride, which often occurs with it but has an unpleasant taste.

Most salt deposits have been formed by the evaporation of sea water, which is 2.7 per cent sodium chloride, or the evaporation of the salty water of inland lakes. Salt deposits are forming today as a result of the evaporation of waters such as Lake Eyre in Australia and the Great Salt Lake, Utah. Salt beds are mined at Stassfurt in Germany, Wieliczka in Poland, Cheshire in England, Siberia and many other places. Salzburg in Austria was named after the nearby salt mines, which were worked in prehistoric times and later supplied salt to Rome.

Under stress rock salt becomes plastic and flows. Salt

domes form when layers of rock salt are pushed upwards by the pressure of overlying bedrock. The salt domes are of importance because in various of the world's oilfields they form oil traps which can be exploited.

Salt is very important as a food and food preservative. It is also used in the manufacture of sodium carbonate for soap and glass making, chlorine for bleach, and water softeners. Salt itself is used as a de-icer on the roads.

Graphite (Plumbago or Black lead) *Native carbon* (C) Diamond, the hardest natural substance, and graphite, one of the softest, are both forms of carbon. Graphite is a lead grey, opaque, dull to submetallic mineral with a black streak. It occurs usually as scales or columnar masses and, in rare cases, as hexagonal crystals with perfect basal cleavage.

Graphite has a hardness of between 1 and 2 and is sectile and lightweight, with a specific gravity of 2.1–2.3. It has a greasy feel and is cold to the touch because it conducts heat well. Graphite can be recognized by its softness, feel and weight, and it is distinguished from molybdenite by its black streak.

Graphite is usually found in metamorphosed sediments which originally contained a high proportion of organic material such as plant remains. Hexagonal crystals occur in some marbles; and graphite deposits in Korea, Ontario and Mexico are the result of contact metamorphism of coal.

The name graphite comes from the Greek word meaning to write, and the best known use of the mineral is in 'lead' pencils, in which the hardness varies according to the amount of clay mixed with the graphite. The names plumbago and black lead were used because for a long time graphite was mistaken for lead. Graphite is used as a lubricant; in electrodes, commutators and paint; for making crucibles and lining moulds for metal casting; and in the atomic piles of nuclear reactors.

Diamond *Native carbon* (C)   It is difficult to accept that this brilliant gemstone is the same element as soft, black, opaque graphite and even ordinary soot. Pure diamond is colourless

Crystals and cut stones of corundum, including the gem varieties ruby and sapphire

Diamond crystal in kimberlite, and a cut diamond

and transparent but yellow, brown red and green varieties are sometimes found, and occasionally blue or black. Diamond occurs as separate crystals which can be octahedral, cubic or dodecahedral and often have curved faces. Diamond has perfect octahedral cleavage and shows brilliant adamantine lustre on broken or cut faces, although crystals when found are often worn and greasy looking.

Diamond is the hardest natural substance, with a hardness of 10 on Mohs' scale, so it can be cut and polished only by another diamond. It can be identified by its hardness and adamantine lustre. Adamant is an old name for diamond and means 'invincible' but despite its extreme hardness it is brittle, and at very high temperatures it will burn.

Prospectors have been known to test a diamond to see if it was genuine by hammering it, which of course destroyed it. Scratching glass is another useless test because imitation diamonds are often made of quartz, which also scratches glass.

Diamond has a specific gravity of 3.5, so it occurs in placer deposits. The gems originate in volcanic pipes filled with an altered olivine-rich rock called kimberlite or 'blue ground'. The blue ground dug from the Great Hole at Kimberley contains eight million times as much barren rock as diamond, so placer deposits where the diamonds have been concentrated are usually more profitable, as in Namibia. Only about 20 per cent of diamonds are suitable for cutting as gems, and these lose more than half their weight in the process. The rest, which are discoloured or contain flaws, are used in drill bits, glass cutters, masonry saws for shaping building stone, and for cutting other diamonds.

The Carat Weight It is said that the term 'carat' originates from the weight of the carob seed (*Ceratonia siliqua*), pods of which were imported into Europe as 'St John's bread'. The carob seed, which comes from trees of the Mediterranean regions, has been used for weighing precious stones for as long as can be remembered. The weight of each carob seed is usually the same, and it is about one-fifth of a gramme. Arabs called these seeds 'kharrab', from which the Greek word 'keration' was derived, then eventually the English 'carat'. Originally the carat was divided into halves, quarters, eighths, sixteenths, thirty-seconds and even sixty-fourths. In addition, the ounce, which had 144 carats, came into use in France as a special weight unit. The carat was commonly used, but its exact size varied from place to place between 0.197 and 2.216 grammes, which led to great confusion. All was put into order in France, Germany and Italy in 1907 with the arrival of the 'metric' carat, which is exactly 0.200 grammes, and this achieved truly international acceptance in the 1920s.

IDENTIFYING ROCKS

Weathering and Hardness When examining specimens it is important to look at a freshly broken surface. A weathered rock may have a patina of secondary minerals, which gives the surface a very different appearance from the unweathered rock. If your specimen is a boulder or pebble, use your hammer to break it open. At an outcrop other geologists may have done the work for you and left plenty of broken pieces which you can trim to the size you want. While doing so, notice the hardness of the rock and the way it breaks.

The sound a hammer makes on a boulder or outcrop often gives an idea of the nature of the rock. Unweathered igneous rocks ring when struck and are so hard that the hammer bounces off, whereas sedimentary rocks when struck make a dull sound.

If the rock crumbles it may be deeply weathered, made of soft minerals or held together by a soft cement. Hard rocks may be igneous or metamorphic, or they may be sedimentary rocks with a hard cement, such as silica. Some limestones also become harder through having recrystallized. If there are visible crystals or mineral grains, note whether the rock breaks across the grains. If it does, the rock is uniformly hard; but if it breaks around the grains or crystals, the cement or matrix is softer than the minerals it holds together. Fissile rocks break into flat pieces; some of these, like shale, break along bedding planes, and others, such as slate, break along secondary cleavage planes. Other rocks break at joints, and crystalline igneous rocks break into jagged pieces.

Rocks often weather in characteristic ways which give a clue to their identity. Limestones and rocks with a calcite cement are dissolved by rainwater. This process enlarges joints and produces grooved and fluted surfaces. Igneous rocks often undergo spheroidal or onion-skin weathering in which successive layers peel off the outside as they rot, leaving a rounded core.

Texture and Grain Size   The size, shape and arrangement of crystals or grains in a rock give a very important guide to identification. The rock may be fine-, medium- or coarse-grained, or otherwise it may be classed as unsorted. The individual particles in sedimentary rocks may be either rounded or angular, whilst in the igneous and metamorphic rocks they may either be granular or else form distinct crystals.

A rock such as granite, with crystals over 2 mm ($\frac{1}{2}$ in) across, is coarse-grained. In medium-grained rocks, such as sandstone or dolerite, the grains or crystals are visible to the naked eye. Fine-grained rocks, for example siltstone, are those with grains that can be distinguished through a lens, but not readily seen by the naked eye. Clay is so fine-grained that the individual particles are too small to be distinguished even under a hand lens.

Outside these basic gradings there are the very coarse-grained rocks such as conglomerate, which contains large pebbles, and pegmatite, which consists of crystals at least several mm across.

Scrape a few grains off your rock if you can and examine them with a lens to see whether they are rounded or angular, all the same size or a mixture of sizes. In a coarse-grained rock this will be apparent at a glance. If the rock is crystalline and consists of a fine-grained groundmass with larger crystals embedded in it, the texture is porphyritic. Large crystals in a foliated rock are probably porphyroblasts which have grown during metamorphism.

A sedimentary rock with fragments of all sizes from coarse to fine may be a grit, tillite, breccia or conglomerate. In the case of grit look for graded bedding, which will tell you whether the rock is the right way up or has been overturned by folding. Tillite is a glacial deposit, containing both angular and rounded fragments of many different kinds of rock, and sometimes ice-scratched pebbles. Breccia

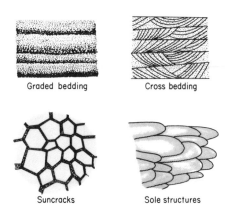

Graded bedding

Cross bedding

Suncracks

Sole structures

SEDIMENTARY STRUCTURES

consists of angular fragments, and conglomerate consists of rounded pieces of rock in a fine-grained matrix.

Rocks made of sand or silt often show sedimentary structures like ripple marks, cross bedding, suncracks, rainpits or slump structures, which all give some idea of the conditions under which the rock was laid down.

Any layering in a rock should be examined carefully. It is most likely to be bedding or lamination, but could be flow banding in rhyolite or foliation in a metamorphic rock. Look at one layer to see if it is straight and even. If it is alternately thick and thin and eventually peters out it is more likely to be flow banding than bedding. Uneven layers can also be foliation caused by the alignment of minerals in a schist or gneiss, especially if there is a sheen of mica scales on the foliation surfaces.

Colour and Mineralogy Colour can be a useful guide to mineral content. In the igneous rocks, the proportion of dark to light minerals is significant. Igneous rocks which contain free quartz are said to be acid and these are generally light coloured, for example granite and rhyolite. Dark rocks such as basalt and dolerite are basic and do not contain free quartz.

Quartz and calcite are both light coloured minerals, but rocks made of them can be dark. The colour of sandstone varies according to the cement. Sandstones may be red if the cement is haematite, yellow or brown if it is limonite, green if the grains are coated with glauconite, or white if the cement is silica or calcite. Black limestones, though rare, do occur, and look deceptively like basalt until tested with dilute acid.

While dealing with igneous rocks, it is worthwhile noting that the weight of igneous rocks will also give a useful guide to mineral content. Acid igneous rocks are lighter in weight, with an average density of 2.7 (with rocks it is more useful to speak of density than specific gravity, although the numerical values are equivalent). Basic igneous rocks have a density of about 3, and some of the ultrabasic rocks are heavier still, with densities as great as 3.4. This can be as useful a guide to identification as the colour, so always feel the weight of a piece of rock in your hand to see if it is heavy or light for its size.

The acid test is another valuable aid, and is performed simply by applying a dilute acid to the rock (*see also* page 44). Applied to a light coloured rock, it will show whether it is made of calcite, which reacts with the acid, or quartz, which does not. Look carefully to see whether the whole rock reacts, or only the cement, making sure to allow sufficient time. Dolomite and hard limestones react very slowly with dilute acid.

Look for well shaped crystals which you can identify. Turn the rock to see if crystal faces catch the sunlight; perhaps two sides of the same crystal will reflect light at different angles, showing that it is twinned. This is often the case with felspars. Granular minerals and crystal fragments are harder to identify but see if you can scratch them or flake pieces off, and use a lens to look for cleavage or conchoidal fracture. If the rock is dry, breathing on it may make the crystals show up better.

Summary: igneous, sedimentary or metamorphic?
If a rock is very hard but not fissile, does not contain fossils and is made up of interlocking crystals of two or more minerals, it is probably igneous.

A rock which occurs in a bedded sequence and is soft or crumbly, or made of grains cemented together, may be sedimentary. Fossils, ripple marks, graded or current bedding, suncracks or rainpits make the diagnosis certain.

A very hard rock with banding, or fissility which does not necessarily coincide with the bedding, is probably metamorphic. Intense folding is another characteristic. Look for the typical metamorphic minerals kyanite, andalusite, sillimanite, staurolite and garnet.

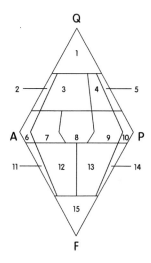

DESCRIPTIONS OF ROCKS

IGNEOUS ROCKS

Agglomerate During a volcanic eruption, lava bombs, dust and fragments of solidified lava and blocks of the rock underlying the volcano are thrown into the air by the explosive force of escaping gases. When the eruption is over some of the larger fragments fall back into the crater and block it, forming a vent agglomerate. Others roll down the outer slopes where they are buried by volcanic ash and may in turn be covered by lava flows.

Agglomerate is a volcanic breccia with large angular fragments embedded in a ground mass of pumice and lava dust. It contains fragments of all sizes and sometimes a wide variety of rock types, and varies in colour accordingly. Although not a very common rock, agglomerate when it occurs is found with lavas and tuff in volcanic areas. The rock fragments are too heavy to travel far so where you find agglomerate, look for the remains of a volcano.

Tuff The rock formed from volcanic ash is known as tuff. Ash is a mixture of sand- and dust-sized particles which are blown into the air during a volcanic eruption. It also includes pebble-sized lapilli, which are small blobs of lava that solidify in mid air. Some ash lands on and around the volcano but the wind may carry the finer dust for long distances. After the eruption of Krakatoa in 1883 dust travelled all round the world high in the stratosphere, producing brilliant sunsets for a year. Layers of tuff often show graded bedding, coarse fragments forming the base of the layer and the finer material settling later.

Augite or felspar crystals which crystallize before the magma erupts may be separated from the liquid part in mid air, to fall in showers on the volcano. Augite crystals embedded in volcanic dust are found around Vesuvius and were formed in this way. When consolidated, the deposit will become a crystal tuff.

Ancient tuffs are often metamorphosed into slates. Tuffs are found with lavas and agglomerate, but may also be deposited many kilometres from a volcano, sometimes in the sea.

Ignimbrite Ignimbrite is usually formed from rhyolite or andesite lavas as these are very viscous and often block the vent of a volcano. When this happens, gases in the lava below the blockage build up until the pressure blows out the lava plug or ruptures the volcano.

The lava inside the volcano contains gases which escape with a rush when the pressure is released and froth up the lava. Gases burst out of the lava bubbles, exploding them into a glowing spray of lava droplets and tiny fragments of glass. This spray, propelled by the incandescent gases, rushes down the flanks of the volcano at a tremendous speed, overwhelming everything in its path.

These clouds of red hot material are known as *nuées ardentes*, and the rock formed by such a cloud is called ignimbrite. In 1902 when the volcano of Mont Pelée in Martinique erupted, a glowing cloud of gas and lava droplets swept down the slopes of the volcano and completely destroyed the town of St Pierre. As the material within the cloud settles, the hot fragments fuse together and form a 'welded tuff', another name for ignimbrite.

Many so called rhyolites, such as those at Rotorua in New Zealand, are really ignimbrites. Ignimbrite resembles rhyolite in hand specimens but can be distinguished from it in the field by its distance from the parent volcano. Ignimbrites extend over a wide area, but rhyolite is too viscous to flow very far.

The degree of welding suggests that ignimbrites are formed at a temperature of about 1200°C. They are usually formed from rhyolite or andesite lavas, that is, acidic lavas with a high viscosity. Lavas of this type often block the vent of a volcano, leading to an enormous build-up of pressure as gases accumulate. The pressure becomes sufficient to burst through the lava in an explosion, forming as it does so a *nuée ardente*.

Rhyolite   Rhyolite is not a common rock. It is the most acidic type of lava, the volcanic equivalent of granite. Like granite, rhyolite consists of quartz, felspar and some mica or hornblende; and it is usually light coloured, with irregular bands of glassy material and microscopically crystalline rock. It is comparatively light in weight, and often has a flinty appearance.

Rhyolite lava is stiff and viscous and never flows far from the parent volcano before cooling. Often the lava cools in

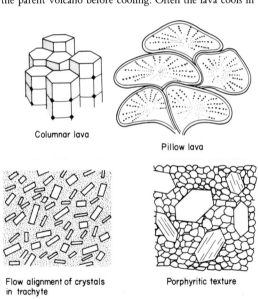

Columnar lava

Pillow lava

Flow alignment of crystals
in trachyte

Porphyritic texture

LAVA FORMS AND TEXTURES

the throat of the volcano without being erupted. When this happens, gases from magma below may build up enough pressure for an explosion, which removes the plug of rhyolite and sometimes the top of the volcano as well.

Some rhyolites contain spherulites, spherical clusters of radiating needle-like quartz or felspar crystals. Porphyritic rhyolite has well-shaped crystals of quartz or felspar.

Rhyolite is always found near a volcano or the remains of one, usually with tuff, agglomerate and pumice or obsidian.

Pumice   Pumice is a white or light grey rock, honey-combed with holes made by gas bubbles as they escape through the lava. It is very light in weight and is the only rock which floats on water. The catastrophic eruption of Krakatoa in 1883 threw out so much pumice that floating blocks were a danger to shipping for a long time afterward.

The stone itself is used in the bathroom as a mild abrasive. Powdered pumice is used in scouring powders, including those used by dentists for polishing teeth. It is also used for rubbing down stone, wood and leather.

Pumice is found wherever there is or has been explosive volcanic activity, and some of the best industrial grade pumice is exported from Lipari and other volcanic islands in the Mediterranean.

Obsidian   Acid lava which contains very little gas may solidify as obsidian, a dark coloured volcanic glass. Obsidian is made of the same minerals as granite but cooled so quickly that they do not have time to crystallize. Most obsidian is black, but it may be dark green or brown and sometimes contains spherulites, spherical clusters of radiating quartz or felspar crystals.

Like man-made glass, obsidian breaks with a conchoidal fracture and is easily chipped to a sharp edge. Like flint it has been used for thousands of years for toolmaking. Large quantities have been taken from Obsidian Cliff in Yellow-stone National Park to make Indian arrowheads. The Aztecs used a great deal of obsidian for tools, including sacrificial knives, the eyes of carvings of their gods, and even mirrors.

Lava (left to right). Back: pumice, lava. Front: trachyte, obsidian

Pitchstone Glassy material which fails to reach the surface solidifies underground as pitchstone. On the Isle of Arran in Scotland there are brown pitchstone sills, and Eigg has dykes of pitchstone. It contains more water than obsidian and tends to have crystals and spherulites of quartz and felspar. In time all glass devitrifies as crystals form, and old pitchstone eventually recrystallizes and becomes indistinguishable from rhyolite.

Granite The most common coarse-grained plutonic igneous rock, granite is a light coloured speckled rock consisting of interlocking crystals of white or pink felspar, grey glassy quartz and a small amount of some other mineral which may be silvery muscovite, brown, green or black biotite or hornblende. Pink or red granites sometimes contain pink orthoclase and white plagioclase but the dominant felspar is orthoclase. Granite may be a mass of

Graphic granite; the intergrowth of quartz and felspar resembles cuneiform or Hebrew writing

similar-sized crystals, but porphyritic granites contain large felspar phenocrysts, for example, the pink orthoclase in Shap granite in the north of England, and white felspar in the grey Dartmoor granite in the west. Another textural variety is graphic granite, in which the grey quartz and pale pink or white felspar grow together into shapes which resemble Hebrew writing. Graphic texture is also common in pegmatites.

Granite forms batholiths in areas of mountain building, and as it is very resistant to erosion it is often left standing as peaks, such as the Sugarloaf at Rio de Janeiro, or low tors like those of Dartmoor. Islands like Rockall and the Scilly Isles, off the coast of Britain, are also granite relics.

Granite weathers eventually to kaolin and quartz sand. Weathering along joints produces rounded surfaces, examples of which can be seen in the tors of Dartmoor and the koppies of southern Africa. At Rhodes Grave in Rhodesia the Bulawayo granite, the oldest granite in the world, has weathered to a collection of gigantic spheres perched on a granite hill.

As the rock resists the sea so well, it is a favourite building stone for lighthouses. Granite takes a good polish and lasts almost indefinitely, so it is a popular stone for buildings of all kinds. It was used for Old London Bridge and the British Museum, and was quarried by the ancient Egyptians for their obelisks. It has been carved into gigantic monuments, like Mount Rushmore in the USA, and is used for gravestones, statues and kerbstones.

Pegmatite Unless specified otherwise, the name pegmatite means granite pegmatite. Other kinds do occur, for instance syenite pegmatite, but they are not common.

The minerals are essentially the same as in granite, for example orthoclase, usually combined with quartz and muscovite or biotite. In addition there may be many accessory minerals such as apatite, uraninite or cassiterite, which are all formed from the rare elements concentrated in the residual magma from which the rock crystallizes.

Pegmatites are usually light coloured, extremely coarse-grained rocks, and the world's largest crystals have been found in them. Pegmatites are also the chief source of minerals like beryl and mica, so they are of considerable economic importance. Single crystals of orthoclase as big as a house have been found in Norway and the Urals, mica books over three metres wide in Ontario and South Africa, and beryls like telegraph poles in Indian and North American pegmatites. Cavities are common in pegmatites, and these are usually lined with crystals of quartz, topaz, tourmaline and many other minerals. Most of the large spectacular crystals in museums were taken from pegmatites.

In some pegmatites quartz and felspar crystals grow together to give graphic texture, which looks like Hebrew writing.

Pegmatite is formed during the last stage of crystallization of granite, and usually occupies fissures, dykes, small sills and irregularly shaped bodies in the outer parts of a granite mass, and surrounding rocks. Many granites however are poor in pegmatites, for instance the great batholiths of the Andes mountains.

Aplite Aplite is a light coloured white, cream or pink fine-grained rock found in thin veins and dykes cutting across granite. It is a very acid rock consisting essentially of quartz and felspar. Aplite is produced in small amounts during the last stage of crystallization of granite, but the melt lacks the water and gases which enable large crystals to form, as in the case of pegmatite.

Greisen Greisen is a rock formed from granite by the action of fluorine-rich gases. The felspars are altered to muscovite, and fluorine-rich minerals are formed, producing a crumbly white or grey rock consisting essentially of muscovite and quartz, with topaz and fluorite. Greisen occurs with only a few granites such as those of Cornwall, the Erzgebirge in Saxony and the granites of northern Nigeria.

Luxullyanite If granite is subjected to the action of

Granite from Shap Fell, Cumbria, UK, showing large porphyritic crystals of orthoclase

Larvikite: a decorative variety of syenite from Norway, showing the pearly lustre of the felspar crystals

boron-rich gases, felspar is replaced by tourmaline and the result is a rock consisting of tourmaline, quartz, and the remains of felspar crystals. Tourmaline is an accessory mineral in some granites, as at Carnmenellis in Cornwall as well as Dartmoor, but if it replaces the minerals normally present in granite, first luxullyanite and then quartz schorl rock are produced. The latter is composed entirely of quartz and black tourmaline.

China Clay   A white rock consisting of kaolinite clay and quartz, china clay is so soft that it can be dug by hand or removed by a jet of water. It is formed as a result of the hydrothermal alteration of granite, in which hot gases, mainly steam, alter the felspars to kaolinite, leaving only quartz and some mica unchanged. If the process does not go very far, enough kaolinite may be formed to make the felspar crystals opaque without breaking them down.

Large masses of granite near St Austell in Cornwall have been converted to china clay and luxullyanite. If pure the clay is used for making white porcelain and if it has a high quartz content it can be made into stoneware pottery. Other uses for the clay are as a filler in rubber and plastics, a coating for quality paper, an anti-caking agent in fertilizer and for pelletizing animal foods. It is the chief raw material exported from Britain.

Trachyte   Trachyte is an uncommon light-coloured lava sometimes erupted with basalt from island volcanoes. The islands of St Helena, Madeira, Madagascar and Iceland have small amounts of trachyte lava associated with abundant basalt flows. In the British Isles trachytes are found mainly in the Midland Valley of Scotland and on the Isle of Mull.

Trachyte is usually grey, but is sometimes white, cream or pink. It consists mostly of felspar with a small amount of pyroxene or amphibole, and the abundance of felspar gives the rock a light colour and also makes it light in weight. Typical trachytic texture consists of small elongated crystals of potash felspar embedded in a fine-grained matrix of more felspar and a little pyroxene or amphibole. The felspar crystals are often aligned in the direction in which the lava flowed.

Syenite Syenite is the coarse-grained equivalent of trachyte. It is usually light or dark grey, red or pink. It is also light in weight and resembles granite, but is far less common. It usually contains orthoclase rather than plagioclase and little or no quartz. The dark minerals are biotite, pyroxene or amphibole.

Syenite forms pegmatites as granite does, and porphyritic varieties occur as well, with large felspar crystals in a medium-grained groundmass. Boulders of the rhomb porphyries of Scandinavia were carried all over northern Europe during the Pleistocene Ice Age, and thus indicate the direction and extent of movement of the ice sheets.

Larvikite or laurvikite is a decorative variety of syenite from Norway. It consists mainly of large felspar crystals which show a blue-green play of colour when they catch the light. Polished slabs are often used as a facing stone on buildings.

Andesite Next to basalt, andesite is the most abundant type of lava. It is a little lighter in colour than basalt; it is usually grey or purplish and sometimes contains visible crystals of plagioclase, biotite, hornblende or augite. It consists essentially of plagioclase and one or more dark minerals. Andesite is a stiff, viscous lava which congeals easily and often blocks the crater of a volcano. Andesite eruptions therefore tend to be explosive and produce more ash and agglomerate than lava.

Andesite is a characteristic lava of young mountain belts formed along the borders of continents, and it is the typical lava of the Andes mountains and the 'Ring of Fire', the series of volcanoes around the Pacific Ocean. It is the dominant lava of Mount Fuji in Japan, the volcanoes of Java and Sumatra and the western USA, where it is found in Yellowstone National Park.

Diorite Diorite is a rather dark coarse-grained rock

resembling granite but with little or no quartz. It consists essentially of plagioclase and hornblende, with biotite in the more acid types and augite in the more basic. It is usually black and white but sometimes greenish or pink.

Diorite is lighter than gabbro and does not contain olivine, and can be distinguished from granite by its comparative lack of quartz. Medium-grained rocks of dioritic composition are called microdiorites and are usually porphyritic with phenocrysts of hornblende, biotite or occasionally augite.

Diorite batholiths are common along the western seaboard of America in Alaska and the Rocky Mountains.

Basalt Basalt is a black or dark grey rock composed mainly of pyroxene and calcic plagioclase. It is usually so fine-grained that the minerals cannot be seen, but in a freshly broken piece tiny needles of plagioclase may just be visible with a lens. Sometimes embedded in the fine-grained mass are a few larger crystals of white plagioclase, shiny black

Volcanic bombs showing spindle shape formed by rotation in flight

augite or green, glassy-looking olivine. Weathering alters olivine and pyroxene to iron oxides, which give the rock a rusty look, and at an outcrop the layers of rock often crumble and peel off like the skins of an onion.

If basalt dykes cool quickly against the cold rocks into which they are injected, they may form a thin edging of glassy tachylite. Another kind of basalt glass is Pelée's hair, which consists of golden-brown glass fibres, blown out as lava spray from volcanoes in Hawaii, where Pelée is the goddess of fire.

Basalt lava is hotter than acid lavas, with temperatures of up to 1200°C. It is less viscous and therefore moves faster, spreading out from volcanoes and fissures in the form of wide, almost flat lava flows. A feature common to thick lava flows and basalt sills is columnar jointing, formed by the contraction of the lava as it cools.

Steam and other gases are dissolved in lava and escape as it cools. If the gases escape in bursts, breaking the cooled crust of the flow into rough clinkery blocks, the lava is called aa (pronounced ah-ah), a Hawaiian name. If the gases escape quietly a smooth skin forms that flows into ropy snakelike ridges and the lava is called pahoehoe.

If lava erupts underwater, it forms blob-like masses which cool quickly with a tachylite skin. At the centre these masses are honeycombed with holes, made by the gas bubbles trapped inside. As other blobs (up to a metre across) are forced out from the same source, a pile of flattened balloon-shaped masses is formed and these are called pillow lavas.

Basalt has always been the commonest type of lava. The ocean floors are made of it and basalt is constantly forcing its way up as dykes and pillow lavas along the fissures in the mid ocean ridges. The Atlantic ocean is actually growing wider as the new rock pushes Europe and America apart. Most island volcanoes, such as Hawaii and the Galapagos, are built of basalt.

From time to time through the ages the crust of the continents has cracked, and basalt has welled up through the vertical fissures to flood vast areas. As the lava cools in these fissures, it sets into dykes. Where large volumes of basalt

Gabbro (left) and basalt (right): coarse- and fine-grained rocks formed from basic magma of similar composition

have been erupted, successive flows may have built up a lava plateau more than 1000 m thick. Examples of flood basalts are the Colorado plateau, the Deccan of India and southern Africa, where the Zambesi river has carved the Victoria Falls out of the resistant lava.

In Britain, basalt dykes are common in the north-west, especially around the ancient volcanic centres of Skye, Mull, Arran and Antrim. These form part of a basalt plateau with an area of 150,000 km² (58,915 sq miles) which includes Greenland and Iceland where there are still active volcanoes.

Basalt is often quarried and crushed for use as roadstone, so if there are no dykes in your area you can probably still find pieces of basalt if you look along the roadside.

Dolerite   Dolerite (or in USA diabase) is a rock of medium grain size similar in composition to basalt and gabbro. It is usually black or dark grey and consists of a mass of tiny elongated white crystals of plagioclase set in a groundmass of dark pyroxene. Sometimes larger crystals of olivine, pyroxene or plagioclase occur giving the rock a porphyritic texture. Spheroidal weathering is typical of dolerite, the dark minerals weathering first to a rust coloured earthy mass in which the white plagioclase crystals sometimes survive.

Dolerite is the common rock of basic dykes and sills and crystallizes underground near volcanic centres where basalt is the dominant magma. Dolerite sills are often very extensive. Examples are the Whin Sill which underlies much of northern England, and the Palisade Sill of New Jersey, which in places is 300 m thick and outcrops for 80 km (50 miles) along the west bank of the Hudson river.

Dolerite is a hard rock, often used for roadstone. Bluestones of Stonehenge were carved out of dolerite, which was brought to Stonehenge from the Prescelly Mountains in Wales.

Gabbro   Gabbro is the coarse-grained equivalent of basalt. It is a dark grey or black rock, consisting essentially of dark coloured pyroxene and white plagioclase. Light coloured leucogabbros also occur, in which there is more plagioclase than pyroxene. A very light coloured rock consisting almost entirely of plagioclase is called anorthosite.

Some gabbros contain greenish olivine crystals but most are black, speckled with white plagioclase. Layering is common and separate layers of dark pyroxene and light plagioclase give gabbro a banded appearance when seen in outcrop, though hand specimens are usually fairly homogeneous. The concentration of dark minerals makes gabbro a relatively dense rock. The dark layers sometimes contain concentrations of heavy minerals like ilmenite and platinum.

Gabbro forms large dykes, and batholiths, of which the Cuillin Hills of Skye are examples. It occurs in sheet-like intrusions several km across, such as the Bushveld Complex of South Africa. The Bushveld Complex is granite above and gabbro below, with some anorthosite in the basal layers; it covers an area of 50,000 km² (19,305 sq miles).

Peridotite Peridotite is an ultrabasic rock. It is coarse-grained, dark and heavy. Olivine is the most abundant mineral in peridotite, usually accompanied by pyroxene, but in some cases olivine-biotite or olivine-amphibole peridotites are formed. A rock consisting almost entirely of olivine is called dunite after Mount Dun in New Zealand, where there is a mass of peridotite, dunite and serpentine which covers 25 km (15.5 miles). Both olivine and pyroxene alter to serpentine, so peridotite is often replaced by serpentine, for instance at the Lizard in Cornwall.

Peridotite is an uncommon rock at the earth's surface. It is usually formed when olivine crystals settle out of a basaltic magma to form a heavy layer at the base of the intrusion.

The behaviour of earthquake waves suggests that the earth's mantle, the layer below the crust, may be largely composed of peridotite. Peridotites in Cyprus and New Caledonia may be segments of mantle rock brought to the surface by earth movements. Volcanoes sometimes erupt nodules of peridotite with their lavas, and these can be found in agglomerates and basalts in volcanic areas, such as the Puys d'Auvergne in France.

Kimberlite An ultrabasic rock of volcanic origin, kimberlite was named after Kimberley in South Africa where it is found in ancient volcanic pipes. It is a coarse-grained, blue, greenish or black rock which consists of blocks of brecciated peridotite, partly altered to serpentine, and fragments of the rocks through which the volcanic pipe made its way to the surface.

Kimberlite is valued chiefly because it contains diamonds, which must have formed at high temperatures and tremendous pressures. Kimberlite pipes with diamonds have been found in Tanzania and Siberia.

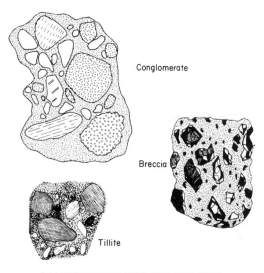

Conglomerate

Breccia

Tillite

COARSE-GRAINED SEDIMENTARY ROCKS

Pyroxenite Pyroxenite is an ultrabasic, usually coarse-grained rock which is dark green, brown or black in colour and almost entirely composed of pyroxene. Some pyroxenites contain small amounts of other dark minerals and a little plagioclase. Pyroxenites are found with basic and ultrabasic plutonic rocks as segregation layers or veins, in peridotites, and occasionally as xenoliths in basalt lavas.

SEDIMENTARY ROCKS

Breccia Breccia is a coarse-grained rock made of angular fragments of other rocks cemented together. Breccia can be any colour and contain any rock type or a mixture of rocks. It has no bedding, very rarely contains fossils and is always found near the source of the fragments. Any extent of transport would have rounded them off and sorted them, forming a conglomerate.

In mountainous areas, rocks that are broken up by frost will roll down hill and accumulate as scree, which eventually

Hertfordshire Puddingstone, a conglomerate with well-rounded flint pebbles cemented by silica

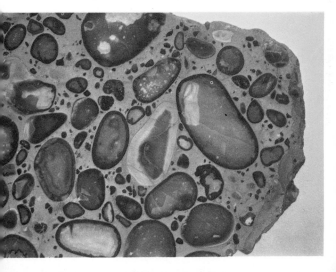

covers the lower slopes. The spaces between the rock fragments are usually filled with fine rock waste and if the scree is later cemented together it becomes breccia. Scree also forms in deserts, where rocks are broken down by alternate heating and cooling.

Other types of breccia are volcanic agglomerate and breccias due to earth movement. Faulting shatters the rocks along the zone of movement, producing a fault breccia. Veins are often brecciated by earth movements and the spaces in the breccia filled with ore minerals. Brecciated marble is similar in origin and often owes its colour to minerals deposited in the cracks. Such marbles occur in a variety of colours and are popular as ornamental stones.

Conglomerate Conglomerate is a coarse-grained rock made up of rounded rock fragments greater than 2 mm ($\frac{1}{12}$ in) across bound together by fine-grained material or cement. The fragments can vary in size from large boulders to gravel so fine that it is almost a coarse sand. Conglomerate grades into sandstone at the lower end of the scale.

Most conglomerates are made of consolidated beach shingle or river gravel in which the pebbles have been smoothed by abrasion. Considerable wear and tear is needed to produce rounded pebbles and in the process soft rocks are usually destroyed. The most common rocks found as pebbles in conglomerate are quartzite, vein quartz, flint and chert, and igneous rocks. These survive because they are hard and resist erosion.

Conglomerate often has a matrix of sand- or silt-size particles surrounding the pebbles, but it may simply be cemented together by calcite or other minerals. The most resistant conglomerates are those with a silica cement, like the Hertfordshire Puddingstone, in which the cement is equal in hardness to the flint and chert pebbles, so that the rock breaks across them.

An ancient conglomerate of great economic importance is the Banket of South Africa in which there are flecks of gold both in and between the quartz pebbles of which it is largely composed.

Tillite   As ice sheets move outward from a cold area, like rivers in slow motion they pick up and carry all kinds of rock debris. When the ice melts this is deposited as a layer called till, boulder clay or drift. Unlike rivers, ice sheets do not sort the debris or swirl it about; the fragments therefore do not rub against one another or become rounded. On the other hand, some of the boulders carried by the ice are scraped along the ground and worn into the shape of an old-fashioned flat-iron, or acquire grooves and scratches called striations. Striated rocks are thus found in the till, surrounded by angular rock scree fragments of all rock types and sizes, ranging from those bigger than a house to the finest particles of rock flour.

Till deposited by ice sheets during the Pleistocene age covers much of northern Europe, Asia and America. As it was laid down only a few thousand years ago this till has not yet become a hard rock. Older tills have consolidated into rock, and this rock is known as tillite. The Dwyka tillite of South Africa was deposited during the Carboniferous period, when Europe and North America were enjoying a tropical climate. An even older tillite found in Scandinavia, Scotland and Canada is evidence for a Precambrian ice age.

Sandstone   Sandstone is a well sorted fine- to medium-grained rock consisting mainly of quartz fragments under 2 mm ($\frac{1}{12}$ in) across but still big enough to be seen by the naked eye. At the limit of visibility of individual grains sandstone grades into siltstone. Sandstones containing larger pebbles are sometimes called grits, such as the Millstone Grit of the Pennines, but the term grit is usually reserved for sandstones with sharp angular grains.

In addition to quartz, sandstones often contain opaque white or pink felspar grains, shining mica scales and fragments of augite, hornblende and sometimes placer minerals like garnet and magnetite.

The further the sand has travelled before being deposited, the better sorted it will be, with well worn and rounded grains. Sandstones formed under desert conditions consist of almost perfectly spherical quartz grains shaped by wind

Sandstone: a group showing colour variation and including green glauconitic sandstone, red milletseed sandstone with haematite cement, and a coarse sandstone showing bedding

transport. The grains in sandstones formed from river and beach sand are usually more angular and include mica and rock fragments as well as quartz. In sandstones made up of sand from glaciers, or river sand which has not travelled far, the grains may be almost unworn and very angular.

Sandstones are well bedded rocks, and show a variety of structures including suncracks, ripple marks, graded bedding and cross bedding. True bedding is indicated by clay partings or lines of pebbles; cross bedding is often at an angle to true bedding, as it is formed by currents sweeping sand over a ripple crest or sand dune, to lie in sloping layers. Graded bedding occurs when a current slackens, dropping the coarser grains first and then finer material. Mica and clay settle out last of all and may form a thin parting between beds, along which rock splits easily.

Graded bedding is therefore a sign that the sandstone formed in water, while suncracks indicate that the water was shallow and dried out at intervals; but cross bedding is less useful as an indicator: it may be formed under water but can also be made by wind in the desert. Sandstones also frequently contain fossils, footprints and worm burrows which indicate the environment in which the rock was laid down.

The colour and hardness of a sandstone is usually determined by the cement. Haematite cement gives a red sandstone, limonite cemented sandstones are yellow or brown, and white or pale sandstones often have a calcite or dolomite cement. Gypsum cemented sandstones are common in deserts, for instance in the Sahara; they are very soft. Many sandstones are so soft that they can be crumbled in the hand, but some pure white sandstones have a silica cement which makes them extremely hard and easy to distinguish from other varieties.

Sandstone is common all over the world and has been used as a building stone more often than any other rock. The sharp grained sandstones of the Carboniferous coal measures, and millstone grit, are used both for building and as grindstones. Sandstones containing little or no iron are used for glass-making.

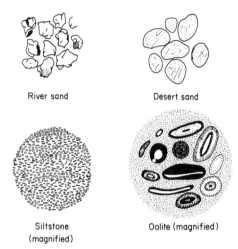

River sand

Desert sand

Siltstone
(magnified)

Oolite (magnified)

FINE-GRAINED SEDIMENTS

Greywacke   Dark grey to green sandstones consisting of
poorly sorted fragments in a fine-grained silty matrix are
known as greywackes. The name is derived from the
German term *Grauwacke* meaning grey grit. The fragments
include not only quartz but felspar, micas, and small pieces
of rock and partly weathered minerals like augite and
hornblende. The larger grains may be angular or rounded,
and the matrix consists of clay minerals, sometimes partly
altered to green chlorite.

Greywackes often have irregularities on the bedding
planes which are known as sole structures. Most sole
structures are scour marks, hollows dug into a bed by the
current which deposited the overlying layer.

Some greywackes were deposited by turbidity currents on the sea floor and contain occasional shells and other marine fossils. Turbidity currents can be caused by storms or earthquakes which start an underwater landslide of sandy mud. The landslide, or turbidity current, flows at great speed down even shallow slopes. Eventually the current slackens, and drops first coarse and then fine material, producing graded bedding. Enormously thick greywacke deposits are found in the Welsh mountains, the Appalachians and the Harz mountains, where they were first named.

Arkose Sandstones which include a considerable amount of felspar are called arkoses. If granite weathers rapidly, felspars may be released and carried away and deposited before they have time to break down into clay minerals. This happens in desert and semi-desert conditions, where there is not enough water in the atmosphere to rot the felspars.

Arkose is a light coloured and lightweight rock which can be cream, pink, grey or red with translucent quartz grains and cloudy opaque felspars. The deposits are always found near the source rock, because felspar is unable to survive long during transport. Because of this, arkoses usually consist of angular grains which are relatively unworn. Cross bedding is common and arkose often contains mudcracks or footprints.

Siltstone Silt is a fine-grained sediment in which the size of individual grains varies from those just visible to the naked eye down to clay size particles. Unlike clay, silt feels slightly gritty when rubbed between the fingers, and when compacted to form siltstone it retains this characteristic.

Siltstone is a mixture of minerals but mica is usually abundant, and minute fragments of mica may be seen sparkling, especially on bedding planes. Quartz is also common, and often alternates with mica in fine laminations. The clay minerals are less abundant, with the result that siltstone is lighter in colour than most clays. It often contains fossils and may have cross bedding, ripple marks, sun cracks and rain pits.

Silt is deposited by water in lakes, the sea or on river floodplains and is cemented by the same variety of minerals as sandstone. Siltstone can be used for building if hard enough, but many siltstones are crumbly. Those which are hard enough and have a marked fissility can be used for paving stones.

Clay Clay is a very soft material which can easily be moulded when wet. It is perfectly smooth if pure and very sticky. All clays consist predominantly of clay minerals, such as kaolinite, which are formed by the weathering of silicates. Clays also contain rock flour which consists of quartz, felspar, micas and chlorite which have been reduced to minute particles during transport. They can be seen properly only by using an electron microscope.

Clay comes in a variety of colours. China clays are white, while those containing a lot of plant material are grey. Most iron rich clays are also grey, although these quickly weather to red, brown or yellow.

Clays can be deposited in the sea or in lakes and swamps; residual clays are formed on the spot by the weathering of rocks. Laterite and bauxite are residual clays formed by deep weathering in warm climates. Where there are marked wet and dry seasons but little soil erosion, all the soluble minerals are washed away, leaving only the insoluble clay minerals and iron oxides at the surface. These form laterite, a red soil which hardens on exposure to air and so is used for making air-dried bricks.

Similar deposits in which the clay minerals predominate are called bauxite and are valuable as an ore of aluminium. Despite its abundance in the earth's crust, this metal was hardly known until the late nineteenth century, when the electrolytic reduction process was discovered, which made it possible to extract aluminium from bauxite.

Marine clays are often very fossiliferous and frequently contain pyrite, septarian nodules and selenite crystals. Bedding is sometimes visible. An interesting form of bedding is seen in varve clays, which are laid down in

Concretions found in sedimentary rocks (left to right). Back: septarian nodule, flint. Front: desert rose, pyrite nodule

glacial lakes. Melting snow in summer washes material into the lake, where it is deposited as a layer on the bottom. The finer particles remain in suspension until the lake freezes over in winter, when they settle out as a much thinner layer. These annual double layers of clay can be counted like tree rings to find out the age of the deposit.

Clay is used for brick, tile, procelain and pottery making; it is also mixed with lime to make cement.

Shale Well laminated clay or silt, when compressed, may harden into fissile shale, if the platy micas and clay minerals lie flat and parallel to the bedding. Shale is a very fine-grained, smooth rock which is often grey, blue or black but can also be green or red. It can be distinguished from slate by its softness and the fact that the fissility coincides with the bedding. It is distinguished from clay by the fact that it retains its shape when wetted.

Lamination may be due to differences in grain size or alternation of light and dark bands. Bedding surfaces often have suncracks, rainpits, impressions of salt crystals, footprints or flattened fossils on them. Fossils are frequently replaced by pyrite, and nodules of pyrite and siderite are common as are calcite veined septarian nodules or 'tortoise stones'.

Shales may be laid down under the sea or in shallow lakes or swamps, like the Carboniferous coal shales. Their colour depends on the minerals deposited with them. Black shales contain abundant carbon from plant remains, and often pyrite. Today pyrite is being formed in the black mud of stagnant waters. If the mud contains little organic matter the iron in the water will be deposited as siderite, red haematite or brown limonite.

Oil shale is a variety of shale with paper thin, flexible and often elastic laminae. It is usually black or brown, and contains a small amount of petroleum, probably derived from waxy and resinous plant remains in the shale. It is expensive to distil oil from shale but when present sources of petroleum are exhausted it may then come to be worthwhile.

Mudstone As the name implies, mudstone is a rock formed from mud or clay which has been compressed and partly recrystallized. It is extremely fine-grained, consisting almost entirely of clay minerals with some finely ground microscopic grains of mica, quartz and rock dust. These are arranged at random so mudstone is not fissile, breaking instead into rough lumps. Mudstone varies in colour and can be grey, green, blue or red.

Clay ironstone is a type of mudstone rich in siderite, which occurs as thin beds or nodules. It is mined as an ore of iron in the Carboniferous rocks of Britain and the USA.

Limestone Limestones are rocks composed mainly of calcite but all limestones contain a proportion of quartz, clay and other minerals. The calcite may be derived from shells, corals and algae, or it may be chemically precipitated in shallow warm water. Most limestones include both organic and chemically derived calcite but some consist almost exclusively of fossil material like the shelly limestones and chalk. Others, such as oolitic and pisolitic limestones, are almost entirely of chemical origin.

The colour of the rock varies from white, cream or yellow in pure varieties to brown or red if the limestone contains a lot of iron or other impurities. Grey limestone is common, and black limestone containing a high proportion of plant material can occur. Black crystalline limestone is difficult to distinguish from basalt at first glance.

Limestone often contains layers or nodules of flint, chert or phosphate and crystals of pyrite and marcasite.

The texture of limestone varies from very fine-grained smooth chinastone formed from calcareous mud, to coarsely crystalline granular limestone; it also includes earthy chalk and the fish-roe texture of oolite. Fossils in the shelly limestones give them a texture which may show up as an extremely attractive pattern when cut and polished.

Limestone is one of the most popular building stones because it is soft enough to be easily worked. This offsets the disadvantage of using a rock which dissolves easily in acid rainwater and therefore is badly affected by pollution.

Oolitic limestone with fossil brachiopod shells

Limestone was used in building the pyramids, and Christopher Wren rebuilt the churches of London with Portland stone after the Great Fire of 1666. Lime plaster is used as a base for fresco painting, and ground limestone is heated and mixed with clay to make cement.

Some limestones are porous and form oil reservoirs, including the Jurassic limestones of Arabia, which act as a trap for oil rising from the rocks below.

Dolomite Pure dolomite sometimes occurs in evaporite deposits with rock salt and gypsum, but on a large scale dolomite is usually found with calcite, forming dolomitic limestone. These limestones probably originated as calcite and were partly altered to dolomite by the action of seawater on the porous limestone, causing recrystallization and shrinkage in the process. This produces a conspicuously jointed rock which is easy to quarry and makes a useful building stone.

Limestone altered in this way usually contains patches which have not been dolomitized, or perhaps the rock is altered but fossils in it remain unchanged. The cannonball limestone of Durham consists of spheres of calcite surrounded by soft dolomite and was probably altered after it was formed.

In polluted areas dolomite is less able to survive weathering than calcite because sulphur dioxide in the atmosphere changes dolomite to soluble epsom salts, which are washed away. The Houses of Parliament in London were built of dolomitic limestone, but the polluted air has eaten into the stone and much of the outside has had to be renewed.

Oolite Oolitic limestones are made up of tiny spherical grains or ooliths, which are a millimetre or less in diameter and usually made of calcite. Oolite resembles fish roe, and the name is derived from the Greek *oon*, meaning egg. Pisolite is a similar rock made up of larger spheres formed in the same way.

Under the microscope an oolith can be seen to consist of

concentric layers of calcite around a shell fragment or a grain of sand. The calcite is precipitated around any small particle which acts as a nucleus. The ooliths are rolled around by the current and grow equally on all sides, becoming spherical.

Unlike most salts, calcite, or calcium carbonate, is less soluble in warm water than in cold and therefore as the temperature rises the water becomes saturated with the mineral, and precipitation is brought about by even slight evaporation. Oolites are forming today in the Red Sea, and in shallow warm waters off the coast of Florida and the Bahamas.

Oolitic limestones usually contain plenty of fossil shells as well as the chemically formed ooliths. These limestones are among the most popular building stones and include Portland stone and Bath stone.

Some ironstones are oolitic, and were either formed where iron compounds were washed into the sea and precipitated with the calcite, or as limestones which were later altered by iron-rich solutions. The chief minerals are siderite and chamosite, but calcite sometimes survives inside hollow fossils. The colour when fresh is green but the rock weathers near the surface to brown limonite.

Chalk Chalk is a very soft white or light grey limestone formed in Europe and North America during the Cretaceous period. It is almost pure calcite with very small amounts of quartz, pyrite, marcasite and glauconite. It is made up of the remains of living things, mainly microscopic oval plates from algae called coccoliths, but also minute shells of foraminifera similar to those which make up some of the deep sea oozes forming today. Larger shells sometimes survive intact, and are often replaced by silica and enclosed in flint nodules.

Chalk was probably deposited in quiet seas at a depth of about 200 fathoms where there was no wave disturbance. It is divided into thick beds, and the divisions are often indicated by layers of flint. It is porous and soft enough to leave a mark on anything it touches, which makes it unsuitable for building but useful for writing. Modern blackboard chalk however is made of gypsum, which is less dusty. Chalk is used mainly for cement making, while some is used in glass manufacture, and some in agriculture for neutralizing acid soils.

Flint and Chert   These often occur as nodules or bands in chalk and other types of limestone. They consist of silica, probably dissolved from sponge spicules and redeposited around fossils or in layers, replacing part of the rock.

Flint is black, brown or grey but the outside is usually coated with a white layer of incompletely silicified chalk. It is hard but brittle, and breaks with conchoidal fracture to smooth chips which are as sharp as glass. It has been used for thousands of years to make tools.

Flint is limited to the chalk but chert is common in other limestones, and also occurs in some shales and sandstones. It is much more varied in colour than flint, but otherwise it is similar and was also used in prehistoric times for toolmaking.

Coal   Coal is a rock that burns because it is made of fossil wood and other plant remains. Most of the coal we use today is derived from giant clubmosses, tree ferns and horsetails, which grew in warm humid swamps during the Carboniferous period.

Normally when plants die they are broken down by bacteria and fungi, but if they are buried before this process goes very far, peat forms instead. In the Carboniferous period swamps, lakes and deltas covered wide areas where the land was slowly sinking, and thick deposits of peat built up only to be buried by flood deposits of mud or sand on which new swamp forests grew. When peat is buried like this it is compressed by the weight of the mud and sand layers above and gradually converted into coal. It has been estimated that at least 15 cm (6 in) of peat are needed to make 1 cm ($\frac{1}{5}$ in) of coal.

The first product of compression is lignite or brown coal, which is soft, still shows traces of plant material and burns with a smoky flame. The black rock we normally think of

Coal forest
Peat
Mud with roots
Sand
Peat
Mud
Sand
Lignite
Shale
Sandstone
Coal
Shale
Sandstone
Coal
Shale
Sandstone

HOW COAL IS FORMED

as coal is the next stage. Further compression and an increase in temperature as the rock is deeply buried results in anthracite, which is very hard, consists of up to 95 per cent carbon and burns slowly with a smokeless flame.

Coal is mined all over the world and is one of the most important raw materials of industry. With modern machinery it can be mined deep underground, whilst even in prehistory a certain amount was dug from surface outcrops.

METAMORPHIC ROCKS

Quartzite A quartzite is a metamorphosed sandstone and as its name implies it is composed mainly of quartz. If the original sandstone contained a small proportion of clay minerals, mica flakes will be formed between the quartz grains. Quartzites are very hard and durable and are usually white or grey in colour.

During metamorphism the quartz grains recrystallize and

Rouge Jaspe: a brecciated marble

become firmly bonded together, so that the rock fractures across the grains and not around them as in sandstones.

Original sedimentary structures and fossils are often obliterated by metamorphism but some quartzites still exhibit traces of original features such as the fossil worm burrows of the Cambrian pipe rock of north-west Scotland.

Quartzites are distinguished from marbles by their hardness and resistance to weathering.

Marble   Marble is the product of metamorphosed limestone. Fine calcite in the original sediment is recrystallized to produce a sugary crystalline texture. Pure limestones give clear white marble, such as the Carrara marble of Italy which has been widely used in statue making.

Impurities in the original limestone are responsible for the many colour varieties. The presence of traces of iron, silica and magnesium produce minerals such as green olivine, pyroxene and sometimes yellow-brown garnet. Serpentine marbles, such as the green Connemara marble of Ireland, are formed by the alteration of olivine marbles.

Marbles are used extensively as decorative stones in buildings and memorials. Marble will react with dilute hydrochloric acid and may be scratched with a knife, unlike quartzite.

Spotted Slates   These are rocks formed in the outer parts of thermal aureoles by the action of heat on slates or shales which already possess an established fissility. Dark irregular spots are produced in the rocks by the growth of minerals such as mica and andalusite, although in hand specimens the minerals are too fine-grained to be identified. Towards the inner parts of an aureole spotted slates merge into hornfels.

Hornfels   Hornfelses are the product of high grade thermal metamorphism of fine-grained sedimentary or volcanic rocks. Recrystallization is complete and the rock takes on a fine-grained granular texture, often with large porphyroblasts of minerals such as andalusite, garnet or even pyroxene. The main constituents of the groundmass are

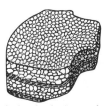

Gneiss, showing layers of
granular quartz and felspar
alternating with dark mica
or hornblende.

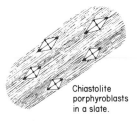

Chiastolite
porphyroblasts
in a slate.

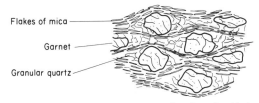

Flakes of mica

Garnet

Granular quartz

Garnet porphyroblasts
in a mica schist.

METAMORPHIC TEXTURES

quartz, felspar and mica. Hornfelses are usually dark in colour, hard and splintery.

The term hornfels is now used by some geologists for any rock produced by thermal metamorphism; a quartzite found in a thermal aureole could thus be called a quartz-hornfels.

Mylonite Mylonites are rocks produced by dynamic metamorphism. They are often laminated due to the slip movements and grinding effects along thrusts and faults. All the original minerals become irregular and streaky in outline, and often the crushing is so complete that no

Phyllite: a foliated metamorphic rock, more coarsely
crystalline than slate

Slate: a fine-grained metamorphic rock which splits along
cleavage planes into thin sheets

individual mineral is visible and the rock takes on a black, flinty appearance.

Typical examples are found along the outcrop of the Moine thrust in north-west Scotland, and in the San Andreas fault zone in California.

Slate   Slates are fine-grained brittle rocks which split easily along well developed cleavage planes due to the orientation of flaky minerals into parallel alignment. In hand specimens individual minerals cannot be detected, but slates consist mainly of white mica, chlorite, quartz, felspar and graphite.

In colour slates vary widely: Welsh slates are usually blue-grey, Skiddaw slate from the Lake District is green and purple, and Ballachulish slate from Scotland is black and often contains small pyrite crystals.

The fine fissility of slates is the most obvious feature and

Garnet-mica schist: a rock consisting almost entirely of garnets in a matrix of mica flakes

often the only trace of original bedding left is the presence of slightly different coloured bands.

Slates are the product of dynamic or low grade regional metamorphism of fine sedimentary rocks, such as shale and mudstone, or fine volcanic rocks such as tuff.

Slates are used widely in the building industry as a roofing material and for decorative work, and they have also been used as bases for billiard tables. The graphite found in the slates near Keswick in the Lake District formed the basis of the local pencil making industry.

Phyllite Phyllite is a foliated rock formed in the same way as slate. However recrystallization is slightly greater, producing a coarser texture; individual mica flakes are easily discernible under the microscope, whereas in a slate they are only just visible even with the microscope. In hand specimens phyllite is distinguished from slate by the silky mirror-like sheen of mica on the cleavage surfaces.

Schist Platy minerals such as chlorite, biotite and muscovite are the main constituents of schists. They are arranged in parallel layers with lenses or bands of quartz and felspar sandwiched between them. This gives the rock a coarse fissility or schistosity (from the Greek *schistos* meaning divided). The same texture is also formed when prismatic crystals of amphibole such as hornblende lie in parallel planes.

Various types of schist occur, and they are named after the principal minerals they contain. A schist composed mainly of biotite and garnet is called a garnet-biotite schist; one composed mainly of hornblende is called an amphibolite, or hornblende schist. The colours of schists depend on the mineral content: chlorite schists are green (sometimes they are called green-schists), biotite schists are usually dark brown or black, and hornblende schists dark green or black. The presence of red garnet often gives the rock a very attractive appearance.

Schists are formed by regional metamorphism where thick sedimentary sequences have suffered intense pressure and temperatures deep within the crust. Eventually they have been exposed at the earth's surface by mountain-building movements. Outcrops of schists therefore often exhibit intense folding.

Chlorite, biotite, garnet-mica, kyanite and sillimanite schists are all products of metamorphosed sediments whereas hornblende schists are formed by the metamorphism of basic igneous rocks which were intruded into the sediments. Schists occur widely in north-west Scotland, Scandinavia, the Alps and the Appalachian chain in North America.

Gneiss The word gneiss (pronounced nice) is derived from an Old High German word meaning sparkling. Gneisses are coarse-grained rocks which display alternate light and dark coloured bands. The light bands are composed of granular felspar and quartz, whilst the dark bands contain muscovite, biotite or hornblende. Kyanite, sillimanite and garnet may also be present. Augen-gneiss (*Augen* is German for eyes) is a variety which contains large eye-shaped porphyroblasts of felspar.

Gneisses are the product of the highest grades of regional metamorphism, and like schists are often intensely folded. Gneisses are found in north-west Scotland and the Outer Hebrides, and occur extensively in southern Finland, the Canadian Shield and in Greenland. The oldest rock yet found by geologists is a gneiss from Amitsoq in Greenland which is 3760 million years old.

Migmatite Migmatites are essentially gneissose rocks which are thought to have been formed by a mixture of igneous and metamorphic processes. They are formed deep within the crust where temperatures are high enough to cause melting. Total melting and recrystallization of a gneiss will produce a rock of granitic appearance and composition. Migmatites represent stages in the process of granitization and textures vary according to the amount of material which has been melted.

The quartz and felspar present in a gneiss are more readily melted, the dark layers melting last of all. A light coloured magmatic segregation is thus formed, which may be squeezed out and injected into the surrounding rocks or concentrated in lenses and pods within the parent rock.

Eclogite   Eclogites are unusual rocks containing bright green pyroxene and red garnet. They are found in lenses in migmatites, as inclusions in kimberlite pipes and in bands in schists which have undergone deep burial and deformation.

The exact way in which eclogites are formed is not known. They may be derived from pieces of the earth's mantle caught up in mountain-building movements, or they may be basic igneous rocks which have undergone intense metamorphism. The high density, and the occasional presence of kyanite crystals, indicate the extremely high pressures under which eclogites have formed.

In Britain eclogites are found in the Glenelg district in north-west Scotland; they also occur in the schists of south-west Norway and in the diamond-bearing pipes around Kimberley in South Africa.

ROCKS FROM OUTER SPACE

Pieces of extra-terrestrial material fall on the earth every day but are seldom found. Small particles burn up as they enter the atmosphere, creating the flashes of light we call shooting stars. Larger fragments are heated so that they can be seen as glowing bodies in the sky, but though their outer layers are melted and stripped away they are not destroyed completely and fall as meteorites. They have a dark fusion crust and are often indented with flow marks produced by melting.

Larger meteorites lose less of their momentum through friction with the atmosphere, but the shock of being slowed often causes them to break into a shower of smaller fragments. If unbroken they bury themselves in the ground but really large meteorites usually explode as they land, forming a crater. Craters may be as large as Vredefort Ring in South Africa which is 40 km in diameter. Fragments of

A fragment of the Barwell meteorite, a stony meteorite with a
dark fusion crust

A fragment of the Canyon Diabolo meteorite, a typical iron
meteorite

meteoritic iron, and glass formed from sand melted by the heat of the explosion, are usually found nearby and at Meteor Crater in Arizona 30 tons of iron have been collected.

There are three main types of meteorite: stones, stony-irons which are intermediate in composition, and irons.

Stony Meteorites   Most of the meteorites which are seen to fall and are picked up afterwards are stones. They are usually small enough to hold in the hand, because they break up on entering the atmosphere more easily than irons. They are grey or greenish inside with a dark crust and consist mainly of olivine and pyroxene with some plagio-clase felspar. There are two kinds. Chondrites contain small spherical grains of olivine or pyroxene, called chondrules, and also a certain amount of nickel iron and troilite. Achondrites contain neither chondrules nor nickel iron. They are coarser-grained than chondrites and some are similar in composition to terrestrial igneous rocks.

Iron Meteorites   Sometimes called irons, these consist almost entirely of iron, with 7 to 8 per cent nickel, intergrown in a pattern known as the Widmanstatten structure, which becomes visible when a polished surface is etched with acid. Meteoritic iron can usually be identified by its nickel content, which is greater than that of man-made iron. An important mineral which is often found in considerable quantities in meteorites is troilite, a non-magnetic iron sulphide similar to pyrrhotite.

Irons are rarer but are discovered more often than stones, because they do not resemble terrestrial rocks and are therefore more noticeable. Pyrite and limonite nodules, pieces of iron, and slag from blast furnaces are often mistaken for meteorites.

The largest meteorites known are irons, as they do not break up so easily as stones on entering the atmosphere. Most large craters are produced by iron meteorites.

Meteoritic iron was used to make tools before men learned to make a fire hot enough to smelt iron ores. A dagger made of iron which, judging by its nickel content, came from a meteorite, was found in Tutankhamun's tomb. For years the Greenland eskimos used pieces of the Cape York meteorite to make knives.

GLOSSARY

Accessory: minor and non-essential constituents in rocks
Accompanying mineral: sharing the same paragensis
Acicular: needle-shaped (see page 38)
Acid rock: igneous rock containing abundant felspar and quartz – at least 65 per cent
Adamantine: like a diamond
Aeoline: wind blown
Alkaline: (igneous rock) with a high content of the alkali metals, namely sodium and potassium
Amorphous: formless, not crystalline
Amygdales: vesicles found in volcanic rocks, originally formed by gas bubbles in the magma and later filled with secondary minerals
An: percentage of anorthite in plagioclase feldspar
Arenaceous: (sedimentary rock) with sand-sized grains
Argillaceous: (sedimentary rock) with fine grains
Arid: climate in a region where moisture is evaporating faster than it can be replaced by precipitation
Atoll: coral island consisting of a reef surrounded by a lagoon
Aureole: contact metamorphic zone around an igneous intrusion (see page 28)
Basic rock: igneous rock containing mafic minerals and plagioclase felspar but usually no quartz
Batholith: large dome-shaped plutonic igneous intrusion (see page 21)
Beds, bedding: layers in which sediments are laid down, originally horizontal but may be folded and come to lie in a steeply inclined or even vertical position
Bioherm: mound of organic remains in a reef, also called a reef knoll
Biostrome: laterally extensive reefs made up of shells
Bituminous: mass consisting of naturally occurring hydrocarbons (coal) or their derivatives (petroleum)

Bomb: lava fragment more than a few millimetres in diameter, ejected from a volcano while still liquid or plastic and solidifying in flight (see page 21)

Botryoidal: resembling a bunch of grapes (see page 38)

Cement: chemical precipitate filling the spaces in a sedimentary rock

Clay minerals: fine grained, hydrous silicates formed by the extreme weathering of other silicate minerals

Cleavage: (a) the splitting of a mineral along planes determined by its crystal structure (see page 41); (b) fissility in metamorphic rock brought about by compression and not usually parallel to the bedding (see page 29)

Columnar joints: vertical joints common in basalts and producing regular hexagonal pillars of rock

Conchoidal fracture: resembling the fracture of broken glass, which shows a shell-like pattern of concentric ridges (see page 41)

Concretion: spheroidal or tuberous body of material aggregate formed in sedimentary rocks

Country rock: rock penetrated by mineral veins or igneous intrusion

Crevice: open or mineral-filled space in rock

Dendritic: branching (see page 38)

Deposit: a particular layer of rocks within a rock formation

Double refraction: the property of some crystals of splitting a beam of light into two rays as it passes through them, sometimes giving rise to a double image (see pages 83, 86)

Druse: a cavity lined with crystals (see page 33)

Dyke: a near-vertical wall-like igneous intrusion (see page 21)

Dynamic metamorphism: metamorphism produced by pressure

Emery: a mixture of finely granulated corundum, magnetite, haematite, ilmenite and quartz

Essential minerals: must be present in order to define a rock and give it its particular name

Evaporite: a mineral deposited from solution by the evaporation of the water in which it is dissolved

Facet: small surface shown by a crystal, whether occurring naturally from growth in crystal faces, or cut on a precious stone

Fault: a fracture in rock along which the sides have been displaced relative to one another

Feldspars: group of rock-forming silicate minerals with the subgroups orthoclase and plagioclase

Felsic: (a rock) containing abundant felspar and/or silica

Ferromagnesian: dark coloured iron and/or magnesium-bearing minerals including augite, biotite and olivine

Fissile: (material) which will split easily into thin sheets

Flow texture: the alignment of needle-like or tubular crystals, formed if the crystallisation occurs while the molten rock is still flowing

Fluvial: belonging to or produced by a stream or river

Foliation: layered structure brought about by the seg-regation of different minerals in a rock into parallel layers

Fossil: remnant, impression or trace of animal or plant of a past geological age that has been preserved in the earth's crust

Fumarole: a vent from which steam and volcanic gases are emitted

Gangue: the valueless minerals found with an ore mineral

Geodes: hollow, uneven-surfaced rounded objects con-sisting of chalcedony with a lining of quartz crystals

Glass: bead-shaped reniform-botryoidal mineral aggregate with a smooth, shiny surface

Gneiss: foliated metamorphic rock corresponding in composition to feldspathic plutonic rocks

Graded bedding: bedding in which each layer shows a gradation in grain size, from coarse below to fine above (see pages 129, 153)

Granitoid: group of plutonic igneous rocks containing quartz

Granular texture: comprising minerals of roughly equal size

Graphic texture: intergrowth of minerals, especially feldspar and quartz, resembling runic inscriptions

Gravel: small pieces of rock, with edges rounded and

surfaces smoothed by water movement

Heat treated: subjected to a process of heating to change the colour, especially of precious stones

High-grade: (a) rich ore; (b) extreme metamorphism

Hook-shaped: angular fracture, particularly in metallic minerals

Hydrothermal: derived from hot, usually mineral-rich solutions emanating from magma

Hydrous: containing chemically combined water

Hygroscopic: readily taking up and retaining water

Igneous: (rock) formed by solidification of molten magma

Impregnation: diffusely disseminated mineral in the pores of a rock

Inclusion: defect or foreign object, gas or liquid, contained within a mineral or rock

Intermediate: rocks with a 52–60 per cent silica content

Intrusion: a body of igneous rock that invades older rock

Joints: cracks and fissure in rocks with no displacement on either side

Kimberlite pipe: pipe-shaped volcanic structure filled with kimberlite rock, that might contain diamonds

Lamination: layers of bedding less than a centimetre thick in sedimentary rock

Lithic: pertaining to rocks

Lithification: alteration of loose sediments into rock

Lode: mineral-bearing vein or fissure

Low-grade: (a) ore containing very little of the ore mineral; (b) metamorphism produced by low temperature or stress

Mafic: (rock) essentially composed of dark coloured minerals

Magma: naturally occurring molten rock generated within the earth's crust

Magmatite: (rocks) also called igneous, formed from the magma. Those developing in the earth's crust are plutonic rocks; those on the earth's surface are volcanic rocks

Mantle: layer between earth's crust and core

Marine transgression: rise in sea level, causing submersion of a land mass and the deposition of marine sediment

Marl: mudrock composed of roughly equal amounts of clay and calcite

Matrix: material in which anything is embedded

Metabasite: metamorphosed basic rock

Metamorphic: (rock) formed in the solid state from pre-existing rocks by changes in temperature, pressure, and chemical environment

Metapelite: metamorphosed pelitic rock

Metasediment: metamorphosed sedimentary rock

Metasomatism: a process whereby new chemicals are introduced and original ones removed by solution

Mineral: a naturally-occurring inorganic substance with a definite chemical composition and atomic structure

Native: (an element) occurring uncombined, e.g. gold or sulphur

Nodule: small, usually rounded body generally harder than the enclosing rock (see page 157)

Nugget: clumps of gold or platinum in alluvial deposits

Ochre: yellow to brown coloured mixture of different iron compounds such as haematite and limonite

Oolite: sedimentary rocks made up of very small spheroidal granules, often of calcium carbonate, cemented together

Orbicular texture: concentric shells of a different texture and/or mineralogy from the parent rock

Ore: deposit of one or more minerals which can be profitably worked

Orogenic belt: belt of rocks commonly characterised by deformation and folding

Outcrop: exposure of bedrock projecting through rock waste and soil

Oxidized zone: layers in ore deposits close to the surface, where weathering produces secondary minerals

Pegmatite: magmatites with large, individual crystals

Pelitic: (rock) characterized by a high aluminium and low calcium content, especially clays and shales

Penetration twin: intergrowth of crystals (see pages 39, 40)

Perlitic: glassy rocks containing irregular, spheroidal cracks which are formed by contraction during cooling

Petrification: process by which the outer structure of plant or animal material buried in fine-grained sediments can be preserved as the organic material is replaced by minimal crystallisation

Phenocryst: large usually conspicuous crystal in a porphyritic igneous rock

Placer deposit: soil, sand and gravel containing grains or crystals of heavy minerals which can be separated by washing

Plug: roughly vertical and cylindrical volcanic intrusion

Plutonic: (igneous rock) which solidifies beneath the earth's surface

Pneumatolysis: reaction of the hot gases, given off by a cooling magma, with the surrounding country rock

Polysynthetic twins: a group of crystals grown in parallel series (see page 39)

Porphyritic: igneous rock texture in which large crystals are set in a finer groundmass (see page 134)

Porphyroblast: large crystal grown in a rock as a result of metamorphism (see page 169)

Pure: metallic minerals in their basic elemental condition

Pyroclast: fragment of volcanic rock scattered by explosive eruption

Pyroelectric: a characteristic of some minerals that became electrically charged when heated and cooled

Regional metamorphism: large-scale metamorphism unrelated to igneous intrusions

Relict structure: structure of the original rock, which has persisted through metamorphism

Ripple marks: small-scale undulations found in the bedding planes of sandstones and siltstones

Rough: minerals or mineral aggregates which occur without a regular crystal surface

Salt dome: mushroom-shaped structure of salt contained within other rocks, usually diapiric

Scattered: larger minerals (xenoliths) with typical distinct shapes scattered or dispersed throughout a deposit or magmatite

Scree: rock waste on a slope or at the foot of a cliff or mountain

Secondary enrichment: enrichment of an ore by weathering (see page 35)

Sedimentary: (rock) formed of sediment, either fragments, precipitates or organic remains

Segregation: separation, usually by sinking, of heavy minerals from a body of magma

Sill: intrusive igneous body which is sheet-like and parallel to bedding (usually horizontal) (see page 21)

Silt: sediment consisting of particles less than $\frac{1}{16}$ mm in diameter

Sinter: mineral deposit in springs

Slump bedding: produced when an overlying bed slumps down into a weak underlying bed

Solid solution: series of minerals in which there is complete graduation in composition between the end members

Specific gravity: ratio of the mass of a mineral to the mass of an equal volume of water

Spheroidal weathering: chemical weathering along joints which produces rounded boulders

Spherulite: small spherical aggregate of crystals radiating from a centre

Spilite: fine-grained, basic igneous rocks richer in sodium and water than basalt, and containing albite rather than plagioclase

Stalactite: cone-like formation, similar to those suspended in dripstone caves

Stalagmite: column-shaped dripstone growing upwards from a cave floor, or features resembling such columns

Stratification: the identifying, visible structure of a rock

Striations: (a) lines on a crystal due to interruptions in its growth (see page 39); (b) lines on a rock scratched by stones frozen into a glacier or ice sheet (see page 151)

Subhedral: grains showing some crystal faces

Sublimation: process whereby a solid turns directly into a vapour by heating, without passing through a liquid phase

Subophitic: (igneous rock) with feldspar crystals partly enclosed by pyroxene crystals of the same size

Succession: series of sedimentary rocks deposited in sequence

Suite: group of rocks that are related to each other by a common origin or process

Syenite: hornblende, feldspar plutonic rock allied to granite, with or without quartz

Synthetic: artificially created crystal, often used as a precious stone

Tectonism: large-scale movements and deformation of the earth's crust

Thermal metamorphism: metamorphism brought about mainly by heat

Thrust: reverse fault, at a low angle whereas a fault is usually near vertical

Tufa: porous rock formed as a deposit from springs to streams

Tuff: porous rock formed as a by-product of volcanic eruption

Ultrabasic: (igneous rock) containing mafic minerals but very little felspar and no quartz

Unconformity: surface between sedimentary strata representing a time gap between periods of deposition

Vacuoles: spaces left by materials in a magma that are easily vaporized, such as water and carbon dioxide

Vein: irregular network of foreign materials, usually horizontal and relatively narrow, deposited in a rock

Vent: gas and steam exhalations, of volcanic origin

Vesicle: tiny cavity in igneous rock formed by a gas bubble

Viscous: thick, sticky, resistant to flow

Vitreous: glassy; vitreous lustre is the lustre of broken glass

Volcanic rocks: igneous rocks developed from magma at or near the earth's surface, such as rhyolite, trachyte, phonolite, basalt, kimberlite

Weathering: the effect on rocks at the earth's surface of the wind, rain, sun, frost and snow

Xenolith: fragment of country rock in an igneous body (see page 21)

INDEX

Page numbers in **bold** type refer to illustrations.

186